What's
Happening
<small>in the</small> # Mathematical
Sciences

Volume 9

What's
Happening
in the Mathematical
Sciences

AMERICAN MATHEMATICAL SOCIETY
www.ams.org

2010 *Mathematics Subject Classification*: 00A06

ISBN-13: 978-0-8218-8739-4
ISBN-10: 0-8218-8739-4

For additional information and updates on this book, visit
www.ams.org/bookpages/happening-9

About the Author

Dana Mackenzie is a freelance mathematics and science writer who lives in Santa Cruz, California. He received his Ph.D. in mathematics from Princeton University in 1983 and taught at Duke University and Kenyon College. Changing his career path, he studied science communication at the University of California at Santa Cruz in 1996-1997. Since then he has written for such magazines as *Science, New Scientist, American Scientist, SIAM News, Discover,* and *Smithsonian.* He has written two popular books in addition to the *What's Happening* series. His most recent, *The Universe in Zero Words* (Princeton University Press, 2012), tells the history of 24 great equations in mathematics and science. He received the Communication Award from the Joint Policy Board for Mathematics in 2012, as well as the George Pólya Award for exposition from the Mathematical Association of America in 1993.

About the Cover Images

Main image: A typical candidate Higgs-boson-producing event from the Compact Muon Spectrometer at CERN. *Below, left to right*: Locations of simulated earthquake centers in a tsunami prediction model; part of a cyclide of Dupin, recently proven to have the lowest bending energy for any torus; a speedcuber solves Rubik's cube in a timed competition, too fast for the eye to follow; forecasted crime hotspots in a "predictive policing" model. *Background*: Crime hotspots (enlarged). Credits: CERN, National Oceanic and Atmospheric Administration (NOAA), Paul Nylander, Dana Mackenzie, Martin B. Short.

Contents

2 | **Massive Breakthrough**

In 1963, Peter Higgs predicted the existence of the Higgs field, which explains why many subatomic particles have nonzero mass. This prediction was based on a mere page of mathematical calculation and an inspired analogy with the Landau-Ginzburg theory of phase transitions. Almost half a century and more than $9 billion later, experimental physicists at CERN finally chased down the Higgs boson, the most elusive quarry in physics. The discovery filled in the last missing piece of the Standard Model of quantum physics, and spectacularly vindicated the use of abstract symmetry principles to discover new physical phenomena.

16 | **Tubing through Hyperspace**

In 2012, geometers in rapid succession solved three open problems concerning optimal geometries of tori (inner tubes). The Willmore Conjecture identified the torus with least bending energy; the Lawson Conjecture identified the torus in the hypersphere (a sphere in four-dimensional space) with the least surface area; and the Pinkall-Sterling Conjecture classified all of the tori in the hypersphere that minimize area subject to a volume constraint. Tubing has never been so much fun!

30 | **Tsunamis: Learning from Math, Learning from the Past**

The great Japanese tsunami of 2011 killed more than 15,000 people in a country that had been better prepared for tsunamis than any other in the world. The tragedy highlighted gaps in our scientific understanding of this hugely destructive natural phenomenon, and even more so in the public's understanding. It also pointed out some ways in which mathematical models got it right, but not fast enough.

46 | **Today's Forecast: Ten Percent Chance of Burglary**

An interdisciplinary team at UCLA discovered how to adapt a mathematical model developed for earthquake prediction to identify likely crime "hot spots." Two field tests of their software were resounding successes, and predictive policing was recognized in *Time* magazine and other media outlets as one of the top scientific discoveries of 2011.

56 **Topologists Cross Four Off "Bucket List"**

Three decades ago, three-dimensional topology seemed like a wild, untamed jungle of disparate examples. Then William Thurston proposed a series of conjectures that brought some order to the chaos. In 2012, just months before Thurston's death, the Virtual Haken Conjecture and Virtual Fibering Conjecture were finally proved, showing that almost all three-dimensional manifolds are descended from templates constructed in an elementary fashion.

68 **Mathematicians Do the Twist**

Rubik's cube, the mathematician's favorite toy, continues to attract new fans and inspire new research. While "speed-cubers" developed new algorithms (and manual dexterity) to solve the cube in less than 10 seconds, mathematicians proved that an omniscient being could always solve the classic, 3-by-3-by-3 cube in 20 moves or less.

84 **The Right Epidemic at the Right Time**

In 2009 the world experienced its first flu pandemic in forty years. Fortunately it turned out much milder than the three great pandemics of the twentieth century, but it provided an ideal opportunity to test a variety of mathematical simulations in real time. Conclusions: The simulations worked pretty well, and communications between modelers and field workers were excellent, but the late delivery of vaccine would have been a fiasco in a worse epidemic.

98 **Thinking Topically**

Topic modeling is a new statistical technique named after its ability to identify topics (such as genetics or climate change) in a large body of documents. While still in its early days, it has proved hugely popular in the fields of "digital humanities" and it might enable social-networking websites to respond automatically and anonymously to cyber-bullying.

112 **Thinking Tropically**

Blessed (or perhaps cursed?) with a catchy name, tropical geometry enables mathematicians to solve difficult problems in classical algebraic geometry by making simple combinatorial models that look a lot like stick figures. This new type of geometry also has surprising applications to string theory in physics, evolutionary trees in biology, and the scheduling of trains.

Introduction

T HE DEPTH AND BREADTH OF MATHEMATICS, and its unreasonable effectiveness become more evident every
year. Two recent major world events point to the useful-
ness of mathematics in preventing the loss of life. Mathematics
was also a key ingredient behind the scientific discovery
dubbed by *Science* the "Breakthrough of the Year 2012".
Advances in pure mathematics continued apace, too. The
ninth volume of *What's Happening in the Mathematical Sciences* presents all these developments, and more, in Dana
MacKenzie's engaging style.

Several major news stories of the last few years have significant mathematical connections. The tsunami that devastated
Japan in 2011 showed the need for better warning systems, the
best of which employ advanced mathematics. By combining the
newest models and better numerical methods, it is possible to
give faster estimates of the strength and direction of deadly
ocean waves, giving people more time to prepare or to evacuate.
The international response to the flu epidemic of 2009 relied
heavily on modern mathematical models in several ways, but
especially to determine the subset of the population that most
needed to be vaccinated to control the outbreak. Meanwhile, in
a less publicized development, several police departments began implementing mathematically based "predictive policing",
which reduced crime by telling police where to be *before* the
crimes could even be committed.

The biggest science story of the last few years was CERN's
discovery of the Higgs boson. After fifty years and a few billion
euros, the physicists confirmed the existence of this fundamental particle that had been predicted in 1964 by means of just
two pages of mathematical computations. In a different link
to physics, tropical geometry, which has connections to string
theory, has become a major topic in diverse areas of both pure
and applied mathematics. Meanwhile, the statistical technique
known as latent Dirichlet allocation has allowed deep analysis
of texts, whether they be literary manuscripts, SMS texts from
teenagers, or bits of genetic code. Of course, mathematicians
had some serious fun with games, successfully analyzing the
minimal solutions of generalized Rubik's cubes.

We cannot overlook developments in pure mathematics,
where some important problems were solved. Once again,
deep advances have been the result of combinations of multiple areas of mathematics, whether it is topology and algebra or
geometry and analysis.

As with the earlier eight volumes of *What's Happening in
the Mathematical Sciences*, this ninth volume shows how mathematics is lively, practical, and even fun. We hope you enjoy
reading this volume as much as we have enjoyed putting it together.

Sergei Gelfand, Publisher
Edward Dunne, Editor

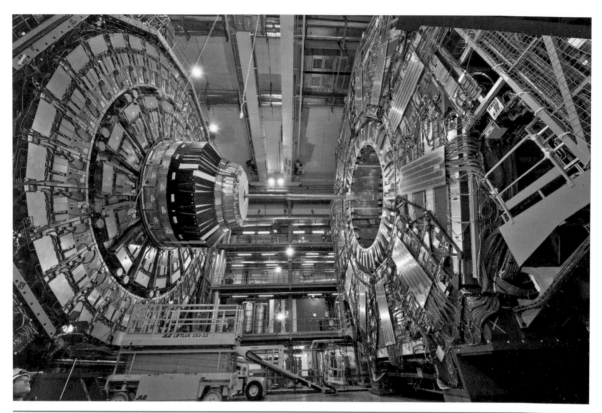

Figure 1. *The Compact Muon Solenoid (CMS) detector, shown here in 2008 just before final assembly. CMS was one of two experiments at CERN's Large Hadron Collider that produced the first statistically conclusive evidence of a Higgs-like boson, nearly fifty years after the Higgs field and the Higgs particle were predicted by a mathematical argument. (Photo © CERN, courtesy of CERN Press Office.)*

A Massive Breakthrough

IT ISN'T EVERY DAY THAT A SIMPLE mathematical idea, which was originally written down on a single piece of A4 paper, leads to the building of a $9 billion experiment. (See Figure 1.) And it especially doesn't happen every day that the $9 billion experiment confirms that the mathematical theory was right. But that is what happened on the fourth of July, 2012, when CERN (the European Organization for Nuclear Research) announced the discovery of the Higgs boson.

The Higgs boson was the last missing piece in the jigsaw puzzle of the Standard Model, a theory of particle physics developed in the 1960s and 1970s that unites three of the four fundamental forces of physics: electromagnetism, the weak nuclear force, and the strong nuclear force. (See Figure 2, next page.) (The fourth force, gravity, has remained stubbornly resistant to unification.) All of the previously observed particles in the Standard Model are either building blocks of matter or conveyers of forces—such as photons, which convey the electromagnetic force. The Higgs, however, stands apart from all the others.

In some sense the Higgs boson itself is of secondary importance; the more important point is the confirmation of the Higgs field, which is commonly said to "give the other particles mass." The Higgs particle is actually a local perturbation in this all-pervading field. The Higgs field does not interact with photons (which are therefore massless) but does interact with the W- and Z-particles, which convey the weak nuclear force. In the same way that the Higgs boson is not just another particle, the Higgs field is not just another field. For one thing, it had never been seen before in the laboratory prior to the CERN experiment. Also, unlike all other force fields, it does not point in any particular direction. It is a completely novel entity called a *scalar* field, which manifests itself as a resistance to acceleration in all directions.

No matter how you describe the Higgs field and the particle that emerges from it, the chasing down of this elusive quarry is a landmark accomplishment for particle physicists, the capstone of a generation of theoretical and experimental work. And physicists were quick to credit the role of mathematics in the discovery. As Brian Greene, author of *The Elegant Universe*, said in *Science News*, "This is an enormous triumph for mathematical methods to make predictions for things in the real world. The Higgs particle has been a hypothetical mathematical symbol in our equations for forty years."

Phase Transitions

But where did this symbol come from? The answer begins in Moscow in 1937, and involves a detour through a part of physics that apparently has little to do with subatomic particles. Physicists have long been interested in phase transitions in ordinary matter, such as the transitions that occur when water solidifies into ice at 0° C. or when iron becomes ferromagnetic when its temperature drops below 770° C. (its "Curie temperature"). Such transitions can often be interpreted as a breaking of symmetry. In an iron magnet above the Curie temperature, the magnetic moments of the atoms are oriented in random directions. An external magnetic field will line them up, but when that field is removed, the random jiggling of the atoms is enough to scramble the orientations again. Below the Curie temperature, the jiggling of the atoms is not strong enough; once you break the symmetry by applying a magnetic field in a certain direction, it stays broken.

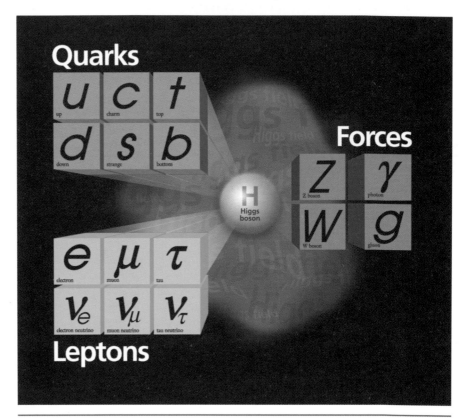

Figure 2. *A schematic view of the Standard Model of particle physics. It consists of two kinds of massive particle, quarks and leptons, each subdivided into six different "flavors." In addition, it includes four force carriers: W- and Z-particles (which convey the weak nuclear force), gluons (which convey the strong nuclear force), and photons (which convey electromagnetism). Photons are massless, but the other force carriers have very short ranges and thus must be massive. The Higgs field (background) was conceived as a mathematical symmetry-breaking mechanism that would explain these nonzero masses. The Higgs boson (H) is a local excitation of the Higgs field. (Figure courtesy Fermilab Visual Media Services and interactions.org.)*

In 1937 Lev Landau, one of the greatest physicists in the former Soviet Union, worked out a general approach to phase transitions that is independent of any molecular details that make freezing, for instance, different from magnetization. He proposed that a material had a mean energy, E, which is controlled by an order parameter ϕ. In the case of water, the order parameter would be the density; in the case of iron, it would be the magnetization of the iron. As always in physics, the material will attempt to find the lowest-energy state to be in.

The simplest case would occur if E were proportional to ϕ^2. Then the energy function is unchanged if the state ϕ is replaced by $-\phi$. (With no background field, the energy of a magnet will be unchanged if you replace all the south poles by north poles and vice versa.) As students learn in freshman calculus, the minimum of the function $E(\phi) = \phi^2$ occurs at $\phi = 0$, which happens to be the unique state where $\phi = -\phi$. In other words, the symmetry of the energy function is *unbroken* in the material's minimum-energy state.

However, Landau realized that more complicated energy functions can lead to symmetry-breaking (and phase transitions). If the energy function obeys the symmetry $E(\phi) = E(-\phi)$ and if it is a polynomial, or more generally an analytic function, then it cannot have terms of odd degree. That means the simplest way[1] of changing the energy function is to add a quartic term:

$$E(\phi) = \alpha\phi^2 + \beta\phi^4.$$

As long as α is positive or zero, the minimum of this function occurs at $\phi = 0$ and the symmetry remains unbroken.

However, if α becomes negative (while β is positive), the graph of the function looks like the curve shown in Figure 3, next page. The minimum energy shifts to a new value of ϕ. Calculus students can work out that the new minimum occurs at $\phi = \pm\sqrt{-\alpha/2\beta}$. The $\pm$ sign is a dead giveaway of the broken symmetry. The system has to choose one of two states, and the physical object no longer reflects the symmetry of the laws that govern it. This transition of the system, from one behavior when $\alpha \geq 0$ to another behavior when $\alpha < 0$, is a phase transition.

A slightly more complicated example occurs if the order parameter ϕ is actually a complex number. Now a good "toy case" to look at is $E(\phi) = \alpha|\phi|^2 + \beta|\phi|^4$. The function $E(\phi)$ is invariant under rotations of the plane, because any rotation of a complex number about the origin keeps its length, $|\phi|$, unchanged. The graph of E looks like a sombrero (see Figure 3). The only state that is invariant under this symmetry is again $\phi = 0$. If $\alpha < 0$, the system is forced to choose one of the nonzero minima of ϕ. The most interesting point about this example is that the symmetry group is *continuous*, so there is an entire curve (or a one-parameter family) of minima. This is typically the case for the energy functions studied in particle physics.

Curiously, the Landau model never was very successful at describing solid-liquid or ferromagnetic phase transitions, because Landau's energy function is too crude an approximation to what is happening at the microscopic scale in those materials. However, it was much more successful at describing a different phase transition, called superconductivity.

> **Curiously, the Landau model never was very successful at describing solid-liquid or ferromagnetic phase transitions,.... However, it was much more successful at describing a different phase transition, called superconductivity.**

---

[1] Adding a constant term would not affect the location of the minima of the energy function, and thus would have no physical consequences.

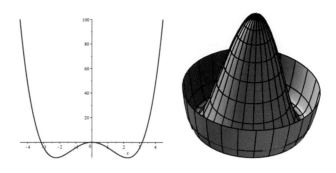

Figure 3. *The Landau energy function was first proposed as a way to explain the ferromagnetic phase transition and later adapted to predict the Higgs field. (a) The energy is a quartic function of the "order parameter" (here represented by x), which measures the amount of symmetry breaking. Here there are two minimum-energy states (corresponding, for example, to a magnet oriented in one of two directions). (b) When the order parameter is a complex number, the energy surface is sombrero-shaped and there are infinitely many energy minima.*

Certain metals lose all of their electrical resistivity at a low temperature; for instance, in mercury (the first superconductor to be discovered) this transition occurs at 4.1 Kelvin (or -269° C.). The most salient experimental facts about superconductors are these:

1. Above the critical temperature, the material exhibits a finite resistance to electrical currents. Below the critical temperature, the resistance becomes immeasurably small. A current that is started in such a material will continue flowing for billions of years, with no battery required to sustain it.

2. A superconductor "expels" magnetic fields, a phenomenon called the *Meissner effect*. More precisely, magnetic fields normally cannot penetrate more than a certain small distance into a superconductor.

3. However, a strong enough magnetic field can penetrate, in quite an interesting way: it punches holes through the superconductor, forming filaments called flux lines that (in some cases) repel one another and form a regular lattice inside the material. This anchors the superconductor in place, a phenomenon called *magnetic pinning*.

As it turns out, all of these behaviors are beautifully explained by the Landau-Ginzburg model, proposed by Landau and his collaborator Vitaly Ginzburg in 1950. In this model, the energy function depends on the magnetic field B and on another quantity s, called the "order parameter," whose physical interpretation was not really known at the time they proposed the model. Later, s would be roughly interpreted as the density of "Cooper pairs" (paired electrons) at any given location in the superconductor. Landau and Ginzburg's energy functional has the following form[2]:

$$E(s, B) = \int \int \int \frac{1}{2}\left[|B|^2 + |\nabla_A s|^2 + y\left(|s|^2 - a^2\right)^2\right]dV.$$

The first thing to notice is the quartic potential energy function, the third term inside the brackets. This potential energy is essentially the same as in the previous Landau model, only slightly rewritten to emphasize the fact that it is minimized at a nonzero value of s (when $|s| = a$). You can think of a as the width of the sombrero-shaped potential energy function, while y is related to its height.

The first term in brackets indicates that the strength of the magnetic field B directly affects the energy. The second term indicates that fluctuations in s are penalized; best of all is for s to be constant. (The subscript A indicates that the gradient is adjusted to compensate for the magnetic field; A is the vector potential that produces the magnetic field B.)

Assuming that B is small, the superconductor will favor a state where s is constant and has magnitude equal to a. It can be shown from Maxwell's equations that $\nabla_A \cdot \nabla_A s = -2ieBs$, where e is the charge of an electron. Because $\nabla_A s = 0$ in the preferred state, the magnetic field B is forced by Maxwell's equations to equal 0 inside the superconductor. This explains Meissner's effect. (Note that this argument would fail if s ever became equal to zero!) Finally, the absence of resistivity, the signature of superconductivity, is explained by the fact that the superconductor can only expel magnetic fields by generating an electric current on or near the surface, which must continue in perpetuity.

One more feature of the Landau-Ginzburg model may seem unimportant at first, but is crucial for the analogy between superconductors and the Standard Model. That is the issue of what happens near the surface, in the somewhat messy transition between the simple behavior inside and outside the semiconductor. Physicists can get an approximate idea of what is going on by studying *perturbations* of the solution away from the "preferred" configuration. Thus, they set $s = a + h$ for a small non-constant function h. The letter h is no accident: this perturbation is the analogue of the Higgs particle, and it is a scalar field. The perturbation analysis shows that h decreases exponentially as it moves into the superconductor, and likewise the vector potential A decreases exponentially. If we think of A as an externally applied electromagnetic field—i.e., a photon—it is mathematically the same as if the (ordinarily massless) photon had become massive. The penetration depth of the photon, which is inversely related to its apparent "mass," depends only on a, the width of the sombrero. The penetration depth of the perturbation h depends on both a and y (the width and height of the sombrero).

Though the Landau-Ginzburg theory of superconductivity seems far removed from particle physics, the key point is that it makes normally massless particles behave as if they had mass.

Though the Landau-Ginzburg theory of superconductivity seems far removed from particle physics, the key point is that it makes normally massless particles behave as if they had mass. This fact inspired all three groups of physicists who proposed, in 1964, what later became known as the Higgs field.

---

[2]A technical note for physicists: for mathematical convenience, the units have been normalized so that Planck's constant $\hbar$ and the speed of light c are equal to 1

Francois Englert (left) and Peter Higgs (right). *(Photo © CERN, courtesy of CERN Press Office.)*

This fact inspired all three groups of physicists who proposed, in 1964, what later became known as the Higgs field.

The Miraculous Year

Early efforts to unify the electromagnetic and weak forces failed because of a simple fact: the electromagnetic force is long-range and the weak force is not. The weak force controls, for instance, the way in which radioactive nuclei decay in nuclear fission or the rate at which they fuse in nuclear fusion. Its range is confined to the size of an atomic nucleus. It's a good thing that the weak force is so weak; if it were stronger, the sun would have burned out long ago. By contrast, electromagnetism is a tremendously long-range force. The sun's magnetic field causes auroras on Uranus, nearly 3 billion kilometers away.

The reason for the difference is that the carrier of the electromagnetic force, the photon, is massless, while the mediators of the weak force, the W- and Z-particles, are heavy (about 86 and 97 proton masses, respectively). In 1964 those particles had yet to be discovered experimentally; that would have to wait until 1983. But it was clear even before then that they could not be massless.

This posed a problem because in any putative unification theory, the masses would destroy the symmetry between electromagnetic forces and weak forces. Ever since Einstein blazed the trail, the paramount choice that physicists make in writing down any physical theory is the nature of its symmetry.

Whether literally or figuratively, quantum physicists assume a universe in which quantum fields live in a vector space that is attached to each point of spacetime. This complicated arrangement, a spacetime with a vector space attached at every point, is called a *vector bundle*. Each vector space, or fiber, comes with a symmetry group of transformations that do not affect any observable physical phenomena. In electromagnetism, the vector space attached at each point is 1-dimensional; that is, the field is represented by a single complex number. The symmetry means that all of the electromagnetic waves passing through a point in spacetime can be phase-shifted (multiplied by a single complex number $e^{i\theta}$ of norm 1) without any detectable effect. Thus the symmetry group of quantum electrodynamics is the group of unit complex numbers $e^{i\theta}$, which can be regarded as 1×1 matrices. This group is called U(1), with the "1" referring to the dimension of the bundle or the size of the matrices.

In 1960 Sheldon Glashow had already proposed a theory of electroweak unification in which the symmetry group would be a group of 2×2 complex matrices called SU(2) $\times$ U(1). The group has four dimensions, which correspond to four force carriers: the photon, which corresponds to the U(1) part, and the three as yet undiscovered carriers of the weak force, which would correspond to the SU(2) part. But in Glashow's theory, all of these particles had to be massless. As his former student Peter Woit of Columbia University says, "At the time, this was a reason not to take his theory seriously."

To make the theory more plausible, physicists needed a way of symmetry-breaking that would affect the particles without affecting the laws of physics. For example, the weak force carriers could have had zero mass early in the Big Bang (when the universe was vastly hotter) but then acquired mass as a result of a phase transition. But what kind of symmetry-breaking phase transition could give mass to a previously massless particle? In the miraculous year of 1964, three groups independently arrived at the same answer: a transition modeled on the Ginzburg-Landau energy function.

The person who has gotten most of the credit for the discovery is Peter Higgs himself, a physicist at the University of Edinburgh. For a pivotal paper in modern physics, his two-page article in *Physical Review Letters* is unbelievably succinct. There are two relevant sentences.

First, Higgs says, "Equation 2(b) describes waves whose quanta have (bare) mass $2\phi_0 \{V^n(\phi_0^2)\}^{1/2} \ldots$ " Here, ϕ_0 is the value of the Higgs field at its minimum energy point, the so-called "vacuum expectation value." This corresponds to the state $s = a$ in a superconductor. The term in brackets identifies the quartic term in the potential, again analogous to a superconductor. *This sentence states that the Higgs particle has mass.* Second, Higgs says, "Equation (4) describes vector waves whose quanta have (bare) mass $e\phi_0$." *This sentence states that the Higgs field gives mass to the (vector) carriers of the weak force.* As in the case of the superconductor, it is worth noticing that the mass of these carriers is sensitive only to the width of the energy "sombrero," while the mass of the Higgs particle is sensitive to the whole shape. This is one reason why finding the Higgs particle was the only way of testing the full theory.

Ironically, most of the rest of Higgs' paper is devoted to a red herring. Like the other physicists who discovered the Higgs mechanism, he actually did not intend to come up with an electroweak theory. He was actually thinking about an electro-*strong* theory that would unify electromagnetism with the strong nuclear force. Alas, the Landau-Ginzburg energy function turned out to be simply an incorrect model for the strong force, just as it had been a poor match for the magnetic phase transition. However, it *did* turn out to be just right for the weak nuclear force! This fact was first established by Steven Weinberg and Abdus Salam, who worked out in 1967

To make the theory more plausible, physicists needed a way of symmetry-breaking that would affect the particles without affecting the laws of physics...But what kind of symmetry-breaking phase transition could give mass to a previously massless particle?

how to incorporate Higgs' symmetry-breaking mechanism into Glashow's SU(2)×U(1) electroweak theory.

Although Higgs has had his name attached to the particle and to the field, two other groups have equally good claims to discovering it. In Belgium, François Englert and his student Robert Brout published first, and are acknowledged in Higgs' paper. And later in the year, an American-English collaboration of Gerald Guralnik, Carl Hagen, and Tom Kibble likewise wrote down the same symmetry-breaking mechanism.

Gerald Guralnik (left) and Carl Hagen (right). *(Photo © CERN, courtesy of CERN Press Office.)*

When it comes to awarding a Nobel Prize for the discovery—which must surely happen soon, given the CERN experimental results and given the fact that all of the discoverers are in their eighties—the Nobel prize committee will need the exacting eyes of an Olympic judge to adjudicate the differences between the papers. (A Nobel can be awarded to at most three people.) The decision may turn on the fact that only Higgs' paper mentioned the existence of the Higgs boson. This sentence ("It is worth noting that an essential feature of the type of theory which has been described in this note is the prediction of incomplete multiplets of scalar and vector bosons") was almost an afterthought, which Higgs did not include in his first draft because he thought it was too obvious. It was only after the referees rejected his first draft that he added it, to make sure that they understood the point.

But leaving aside the sure-to-be-controversial decision of the Nobel committee, what *is* the Higgs mechanism? How does it endow particles with mass? Physicists have struggled to provide understandable explanations for the public. "Walking through treacle" or "walking through molasses" are popular analogies. A truly inspired analogy, which Higgs has said "I object to the least," was suggested by David Miller, a University College London physicist who compared the Higgs field to a crowd of constituents around a politician, which slows her down as she crosses the room. This analogy captures the fact that different particles can interact with the Higgs field with different strengths, because a prime minister would naturally attract a greater crowd than a regular member of Parliament.

Another way to describe the process is to use Feynman diagrams. In physics, fourth-degree terms in the energy function correspond to interactions of four particles—i.e., a collision where two particles come in and two particles come out. The quartic Higgs potential assigns energy to an interaction where a particle encounters the Higgs field and bounces off. But according to the Higgs mechanism, in a vacuum the Higgs field is constant and has a nonzero vacuum expectation value equal to ϕ_0. Thus the particle interacts with the Higgs field constantly, with an equal strength at all places and times. Consequently, it makes sense to simply view the energy of the interaction as a property of the particle itself: its mass.

The Experimental Denouement

Curiously, from the theoretical point of view the story of the Higgs boson ends around 1967, or at any rate by 1973, when the Standard Model reached its current form. "To me, one weird thing is that we are talking about the Higgs particle as a new discovery, and yet from the theorist's point of view it's an old story, something that we have all known since grad school," says Woit.

Figure 4. *One of the most ambitious (and expensive) scientific experiments ever, the Large Hadron Collider straddles the boundary between Switzerland and France, forming a ring with a 27-kilometer circumference. Two beams of protons collide at energies up to 8 trillion electron votes, producing a shower of subatomic particles. These enter the CMS and ATLAS detectors, which are located on opposite sides of the LHC, in France and Switzerland respectively. (Photo ©CERN, courtesy of CERN Press Office.)*

From the experimentalist's point of view, the excitement only began in 1973. The Higgs particle has been their Holy Grail for many years, remaining elusive even as the other particles in the Standard Model showed up one by one. Leon Lederman, the discoverer of the bottom quark, wrote a popular book about the Higgs in 1993 called *The God Particle*, saying, "The publisher wouldn't let us call it the G*damn Particle, though that might be a more appropriate title, given its villainous nature and the expense it is causing."

Indeed, the search grew into a mammoth enterprise. The search for the Higgs was one of the motivations behind the Superconducting Supercollider (SSC), a collider that was cancelled in 1993 but would have been larger even than CERN's Large Hadron Collider (LHC). Its estimated cost had ballooned to $12 billion when it was abandoned. In hindsight, the SSC would have been able to find the Higgs particle. Another experiment, Fermilab's Tevatron (which was less powerful than the LHC), came tantalizingly close before it was shut down in 2011 for budgetary reasons. In its last-ditch attempt to find the Higgs, Fermilab found results indicative of a new particle, but they were not statistically significant enough, in the conservative culture of particle physics, to claim a discovery.

It took ten years to build the Large Hadron Collider, the world's most powerful particle collider, which went online in 2008. (See Figure 4.) Even after that, an equipment failure kept it from collecting useful data until 2010. The two experiments that are charged with looking for the Higgs, called ATLAS (for A Toroidal LHC ApparatuS) and CMS (for the more conventionally named Compact Muon Solenoid), each employ more than 3000 physicists.

The LHC would create Higgs particles by smashing protons together at extremely high energies (3.5 trillion electron volts in 2011, 8 trillion electron volts in 2012, and in the future as

Figure 5a. *An event recorded at the CMS detector in 2012 that would be consistent with the decay of a Higgs particle into two photons (red cones). The same image could be produced by other Standard Model processes. However, physicists saw a greater than "background" frequency of this type of event, implying that in some cases a Higgs particle was produced. (Photo © CERN, courtesy of CERN Press Office.)*

many as 14 trillion electron volts). Amidst the debris of these collisions, a Higgs particle would occasionally be created. By 2012, theorists estimated that the mass of the Higgs (if it existed) would lie between 114 billion electron volts and 169 billion electron volts, or between 121 and 180 proton masses. If it seems a bit odd to create a particle with (potentially) the mass of 180 protons by colliding two protons together, the explanation is that most of the mass comes from the kinetic energy of the protons, which is converted to mass by Einstein's famous formula $E = mc^2$. With 8 trillion electron volts available, the LHC has plenty of energy to go around.

Such a massive particle, however, would be very unstable, and would decay into a fireworks display of other particles. The Higgs particle cannot be seen directly, but ATLAS and CMS detectors look for five telltale types of decay: a decay into two high-energy photons, or gamma rays; into two Z's, which would further decay into four electrons or muons; into two W's; into two bottom quarks; and into two tau particles. (See Figures 5a and 5b.) Each of these "channels" constitutes an independent test for the existence and mass of the Higgs boson. The gamma and Z channels allow the most sensitive determination of mass. The gamma channel is particularly important because it provides information about the spin of the particle. A fermion (a particle with half-integer spin) or a particle with spin 1 cannot decay

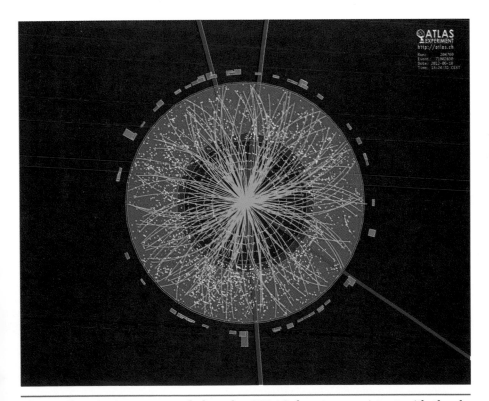

Figure 5b. *An image recorded at the ATLAS detector consistent with the decay of a Higgs into two Z particles, which then decay into four muons. The same disclaimers apply: This particular collision may not have produced a Higgs, but with very high probability some similar collisions did. (Photo © CERN, courtesy of CERN Press Office.)*

into two gamma rays. So a strong signal in the gamma channel would be suggestive of a scalar particle (with spin 0).

Finally, an important point to realize is that no single collision ever produces definitive evidence of a Higgs (or any other indirectly-observed particle). The reason is that there are many other processes in the Standard Model that could result in the same fireworks display. Thus the theoretical physicists have to work out how often a particular event would be expected to occur in the Standard Model *without* the Higgs—the "background rate." (This can be done, for example, by letting the Higgs mass approach infinity.) Then they perform a statistical analysis to determine whether the number actually seen is significantly higher or lower than the expectation. The long-existing gold standard for announcing the discovery of a new particle is a five-sigma deviation from the background, where sigma (the standard deviation) is a measure of the experimental error. According to statistical theory, chance variations would produce a deviation that large only once in every three million experiments.

At this point it might be wise to inject a word of caution. Statistical tests can only give you an estimate of the likelihood of a *random* error—the probability that you just got lucky and happened to detect more gamma rays than usual. It does not, however, control for *systematic* error—the probability that you have set up the experiment wrong. Physicists got a painful reminder of this fact in 2011, when an experiment called OPERA

Joe Incandela and Fabiola Gianotti. *(Photo © CERN, courtesy of CERN Press Office.)*

in Italy reported an anomalous detection of neutrinos that traveled faster than light. The result was statistically significant at the *six*-sigma level, and attracted a lot of media attention, yet few physicists really believed it. Sure enough, it turned out that the anomaly was due to a fiber-optic cable that had not been screwed in all the way. How can you quantify the probability of such a mistake, especially in an experiment as complicated as CMS or ATLAS?

On July 4, 2012, CERN held a press conference at which Fabiola Gianotti (for ATLAS) and Joseph Incandela (for CMS) announced their results through early June. Both of them found a "Higgs-like" particle, with a statistical significance level of five sigma. (See Figure 6.) But what is perhaps most convincing is the fact that the two collaborations had been kept in the dark about each other's results. The fact that two independent experiments reported a five-sigma deviation from the background—and at nearly identical masses, about 133 proton masses for CMS and 134 proton masses for ATLAS—makes systematic error highly unlikely. It also increases the significance of the results, in the absence of systematic errors, to well over six sigma. Gianotti and Incandela could not mention this in their reports because they were not supposed to know about the other team's results.

Thus, it was up to CERN's director, Rolf-Dieter Heuer, to put two and two together. "When I saw the first plot from Joe and the first plot from Fabiola, I thought 'OK, we have it,'" he told *TIME* magazine. "They didn't know their own discovery. I had to spell it out to them. They were very resistant to use the word *discovery*, but I persuaded them, yes, it is a discovery."

The discovery of a Higgs-like particle is probably not the end of the story—or if it is, physicists will be very disappointed. Since 1973, theorists have worked out innumerable variations and extensions of the Standard Model. One of the most intensively studied, called the Minimal Supersymmetric Standard Model, requires the existence of *five* Higgses. Thus the biggest question for theorists is not *whether* there is a Higgs, but *how many* there are. Also, over the next few years at LHC, physicists will look carefully at the decay rates in the different channels to see whether there are any discrepancies between the Higgs they have caught and the one that theory predicted. Those would be clues to the eagerly awaited physics beyond the Standard Model.

But on their day of greatest triumph, physicists were not overly concerned about those questions. After Gianotti and Incandela finished their presentations, the crowd in the auditorium at CERN gave them a standing ovation. As Peter Higgs, who was in attendance, said later, "It was more like the end of a football match than a scientific meeting!"

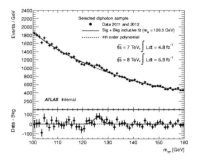

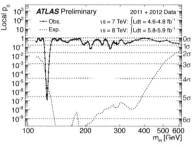

Figure 6. *Two ways of viewing the ATLAS results. (Top) Number of events recorded (solid curve) versus "background" events that would be observed in absence of Higgs particle (dashed curve). (Bottom) The data from the top figure, plotted in probability space. The solid curve shows that the probability of the observed excess of events is less than 3 in 10 million, or "5 sigma," commonly accepted as the threshold for claiming a discovery in particle physics. Independent results from CMS were quite similar, and the joint significance level of the two experiments is better than 6 sigma. (Photo © CERN, courtesy of CERN Press Office.)*

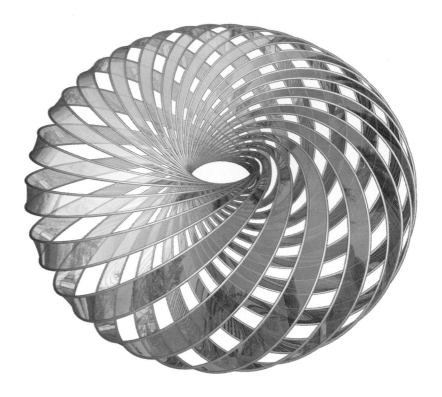

Figure 1. *A Willmore torus with minimum possible bending energy (top), and a conformally equivalent torus with the same bending energy, called a cyclide of Dupin (bottom). Both of these tori are projections of a "flat torus" in four-dimensional space, called the Clifford torus. (Figures courtesy of Paul Nylander.)*

Tubing Through Hyperspace

I F YOU HAVE EVER BLOWN SOAP BUBBLES, you might have wondered why every single one of them is perfectly round. Like Model T Fords, which came in only one color (black), single soap bubbles come in only one shape (spherical).

Wouldn't it be nice if you could make a soap bubble in the shape of an inner tube, or with two or more holes? But any bubble that started out in that shape would quickly round itself out into a sphere. The reason is that a bubble will always try to decrease its surface area, but it cannot change the volume of air trapped inside it. So it will change its shape. Even if it started out in the shape of an inner tube, it would very quickly move toward a spherical shape, which has a lot less surface area.

However, inner tubes *are* feasible if you modify the physics, or the mathematics, a little bit. For example, a lipid membrane (the type of membrane that forms the outer surface of a cell) typically has a shape that minimizes bending energy rather than surface area. As a result, lipid vesicles (i.e., closed membranes) can assume a variety of shapes that are different from soap bubbles. They can, for example, take a dimpled shape that looks roughly like a red blood cell. And they also can form stable inner tubes or even shapes with two holes, like a button.

Surfaces that minimize bending energy, at least in competition with nearby surfaces, are called Willmore surfaces, after Thomas Willmore, a mathematician at Durham University. In 1965, Willmore asked what is the least possible bending energy for an inner tube, and what is its corresponding shape? He conjectured that the answer was an inner tube whose inner diameter is exactly $(3 - \sqrt{2})$ times (or about 17 percent) as large as its outer diameter. It has a bending energy of $2\pi^2$, as do a whole family of closely-related surfaces called cyclides of Dupin. (See Figure 1)

This problem did not appear to be overwhelmingly difficult. "It always seemed that a little more work would solve it, and that kept interest in the problem high," says Robert Bryant of the Mathematical Sciences Research Institute in Berkeley. Yet for more than 45 years it resisted solution. Finally, in February 2012, Fernando Marques of IMPA in Brazil and Andre Neves of Imperial College London announced a proof.

Coincidentally, another closely-related open problem was solved just over a month later. This problem, called the Lawson conjecture, modifies the soap-bubble problem in a slightly different way. Instead of changing the physics, it changes the surrounding space. Blaine Lawson was interested in closed surfaces of minimal area in the hypersphere (the three-dimensional version of an ordinary, two-dimensional sphere). This has the advantage of making it possible to treat soap "bubbles" and soap "films" more equally. A soap film is different from a soap bubble because it has equal air pressure on both sides. In ordinary space, a soap film can never close up. But in the hypersphere, it can. Lawson had found a variety of

Tom Willmore. *(Photo courtesy of Durham University.)*

Haizhong Li. *(Photo courtesy of Haizhong Li.)*

soap films of various topologies, having two holes or more. But he could only find one such inner tube: a surface known as the Clifford torus. He conjectured that it was in fact unique. The connection with Willmore's problem is that its solution, too, is a disguised version of the Clifford torus.

In April 2012, Simon Brendle of Stanford University proved that the Clifford torus is indeed the only torus-shaped *soap film* in the hypersphere. Later in the same month, Haizhong Li of Tsinghua University in China and Ben Andrews of Australia National University used a different version of Brendle's idea to classify all torus-shaped "soap bubbles" in the hypersphere. All of the concepts in these three theorems—Willmore surfaces, soap bubbles and soap films—are very closely related; the reader may wish to consult Table 1 to keep them straight, as well as corresponding theorems of Marques/Neves, Brendle, and Andrews/Li.

A Mind-Bending, Surface-Bending Journey

To understand the Willmore conjecture, you need to understand a few things about the bending of surfaces, a topic that is trickier than it seems.

The curvature of a *curve* is easy to describe. At any given point, you find the circle that most closely approximates that curve (called the osculating circle, from the Latin word for "kiss"). The curvature is the reciprocal of the radius of the osculating circle. Thus a circle of radius 2 would have curvature $1/2$, while a circle of radius $1/3$ would have curvature 3.

For surfaces, the situation is not so clear. At any point in a surface, there are actually two directions, perpendicular to each other, that have the minimum and maximum turning radius. The curvature of the surface's cross sections in those directions, λ_1 and λ_2, are called the "principal curvatures." Note that the surface can bend in opposite ways in these two directions (this is what happens at a "saddle point"). In this case the principal curvatures have opposite signs. In a minimal surface[1], the principal curvatures are equal and opposite at every point.

Back in the 1800s, mathematicians realized that certain combinations of the principal curvatures give a lot of geometric information about the surface. The average of the principal curvatures, $(\lambda_1 + \lambda_2)/2$, is called the *mean curvature* and often denoted H. The bending energy of a surface S, which appears in Willmore's conjecture, is defined by integrating the *square* of the mean curvature over the entire surface:

$$W(S) = \iint_S H^2(x)\,dA.$$

Soap films have zero mean curvature, and therefore also zero bending energy. On the other hand, soap bubbles, which must enclose a certain volume of trapped air, have constant

---

[1]There is a subtle difference between the words "minimal" and "minimizing," both for area and for bending energy. A *minimal* surface satisfies the Euler-Lagrange equations for area minimization, and a *Willmore* surface satisfies the Euler-Lagrange equations for bending-energy minimization. Roughly speaking, this means that they outperform any "nearby" surfaces. In general it is much easier to show a surface is minimal than minimizing, because this can be checked by local computations.

Type of Surface	Minimal (Zero Mean Curvature)	Constant Mean Curvature	Willmore
Minimizes	Area (boundary constraint)	Area (volume constraint)	Bending Energy (boundary constraint)
Real-World Analogue	Soap film	Soap bubble	Lipid membrane
Shape Restrictions (known)	Cannot be closed	If closed, must be a round sphere Cannot be an embedded torus Can be an infinite tube (Delaunay surface)	Can be closed Can be an indented sphere Can be a torus (with one or more holes)
Shape Restrictions (conjectured)			If a torus, must be conformally equivalent to Clifford torus (Willmore, 1965)
Conjecture proved by			**Marques and Neves, 2012**

Type of Surface	Minimal (Zero Mean Curvature)	Constant Mean Curvature	Willmore
Minimizes	Area (boundary constraint)	Area (volume constraint)	Area + Bending Energy (boundary constraint)
Shape Restrictions (known)	Can be closed Can be a torus (with one or more holes) Is a Willmore surface too	Can be closed Can be a torus	Projects stereographically to a Willmore surface in Euclidean three-space
Shape Restrictions (conjectured)	If an embedded torus, must be a Clifford torus (Lawson, 1970)	If an embedded torus, must be a surface of revolution and either Clifford-like or Delaunay-like (Pinkall and Sterling, 1989)	Must be conformally equivalent to a Clifford torus (Willmore, 1965)
Conjecture proved by	**Brendle, 2012**	**Andrews and Li, 2012** Unexpected bonus: if curvature = $1/\sqrt{3}$, must be Clifford-like	**Marques and Neves, 2012**

Table 1. *"Scorecard" for minimal, constant mean curvature (CMC), and Willmore surfaces. The three types of surfaces are closely related, and each one was the subject of a major theorem proved in 2012.*

mean curvature, which means that the H in the above formula does not vary from point to point. These especially simple types of surfaces—minimal and constant mean curvature (CMC) surfaces, or more informally "soap films" and "soap bubbles"—have been studied intensively by geometers since the nineteenth century. Minimal surfaces ("soap films") can never close up to enclose a volume and hence they cannot form bubbles, but they can form interesting unbounded shapes such as the catenoid, the helicoid, and the Costa-Hoffman-Meeks surface (see Figure 2, next page). CMC surfaces ("soap bubbles") *can* close up; but aside from the sphere, they can only do so at the cost of producing self-intersections. Alternatively, they can form infinitely long undulating cylinders called Delaunay surfaces.

Minimal surfaces, with $H = 0$, would seem like logical candidates for minimizing the bending energy. However, if you want a *closed* surface with least bending energy, a soap film won't do, because it can't close up. What you need is a soap *bubble*.

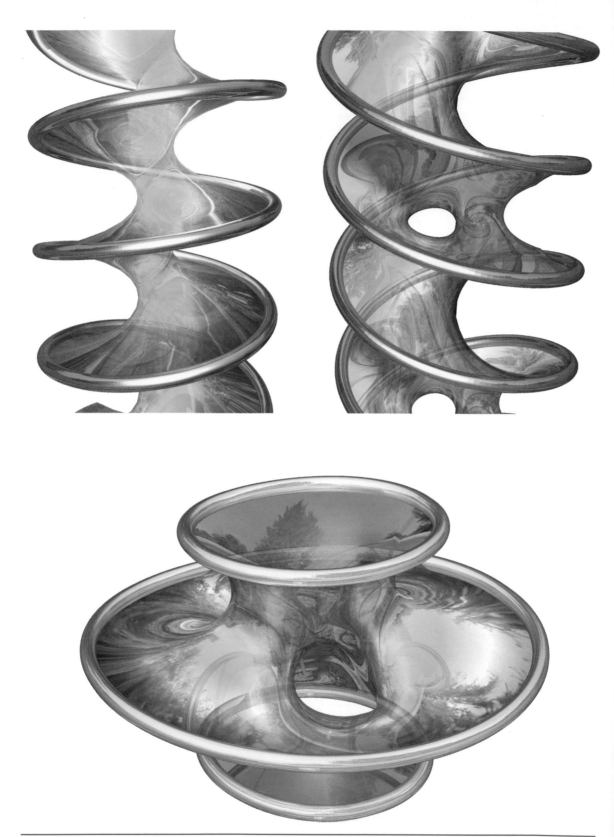

Figure 2. *Examples of minimal surfaces, or "soap films". Top left: Helicoid. Top right: Punctured helicoid. Bottom: Costa-Hoffman-Meeks surface. (Figures courtesy of Paul Nylander.)*

Indeed, any sphere has bending energy 4π, and this is the least possible for any closed surface.

Now what torus-shaped surface has the least bending energy? It can't be a soap bubble, because as already mentioned, soap bubbles can't form inner tubes. Nevertheless, there is an obvious candidate—obvious, that is, if you are ready to move up to the fourth dimension.

The hypersphere (the surface in four-dimensional space defined by the equation $x^2 + y^2 + z^2 + w^2 = 1$) is related to Euclidean space in the same way that the ordinary sphere is related to a flat plane. If you put a light bulb at the north pole of a sphere, you can project any point in the sphere down to its "shadow" in the plane—except for the north pole itself, which has no shadow and corresponds to a mythical "point at infinity." Likewise, if you put a light bulb at the north pole of the hypersphere, you can project any other point $\tilde{x}$ in the hypersphere down to its shadow x in three-space, and you can project any surface $\tilde{S}$ in the hypersphere down to a shadow surface S in three-space.

A big difference between the hypersphere and Euclidean space is that minimal surfaces ("soap films") *can* close up in the hypersphere. When you project these down to three-space, they are automatically Willmore surfaces. The projection sets up a symbiotic relationship between bending energy and area. Let's call $\tilde{S}$, the surface in the hypersphere, a "template" and S, the surface in ordinary space, its "shadow." Then the bending energy of the shadow is the same as the bending energy of the template *plus* the area of the template. (It will be convenient to call this combination the "Willmore energy.") Symbolically,

$$\iint_S H^2 \, dA = \iint_{\tilde{S}} (1 + \tilde{H}^2) \, d\tilde{A}.$$

In particular, if the template $\tilde{S}$ is a minimal surface in the hypersphere, then $\tilde{H} = 0$, and so for such surfaces the bending energy of the shadow is equal to the area of the template.

The Clifford torus is essentially a "square" whose sides are circles instead of line segments. It's hard to visualize because it can only exist in four-dimensional space; but it consists of all the points in the hypersphere such that both $x^2 + y^2$ and $z^2 + w^2$ are equal to $1/2$. Its principal curvatures are $\pm 1/\sqrt{2}$, so the mean curvature is 0 and the Clifford torus is minimal. Because it is a Cartesian product of two circles with circumference $\pi\sqrt{2}$, its area is $(\pi\sqrt{2})(\pi\sqrt{2}) = 2\pi^2$. According to the above formula, if $\tilde{S}$ is the Clifford torus, then its shadow S in three-space has bending energy $2\pi^2$.

With these preliminaries, it is easy to see what the Willmore conjecture and the Lawson conjecture have to do with one another. The Lawson conjecture says that the Clifford torus is the "best" torus in the hypersphere for minimizing area; the Willmore conjecture says that its shadow is the "best" torus in Euclidean space for minimizing bending energy.

There is one complication: Willmore surfaces actually come in families. That's because the "light bulb" that we use to project the hypersphere down to Euclidean space can be put in different places. No matter where we position the light bulb with respect to the template surface $\tilde{S}$, its shadow surface S

Andre Neves. *(Photo courtesy of Andre Neves.)*

Fernando Marques. *(Photo courtesy of Fernando Marques.)*

will have the same bending energy. This is true even though the shape and size of the shadow surface *S* can vary quite dramatically, just as your shape in a funhouse mirror can change dramatically as you move around. Both of the shapes shown on page 16 are shadows of the Clifford torus, with the same bending energy.

Willmore surfaces can also be magnified by any factor without affecting the bending energy. Thus, in fact, every surface comes with a four-parameter family of "conformally equivalent" surfaces that have the same bending energy. Three parameters have to do with the choice of a north pole, and the fourth is a choice of magnification factor.

It is somewhat daunting to realize that our familiar, three-dimensional space is actually a distorted, funhouse-mirror version of a simpler hyperspherical reality! However, the existence of this four-parameter family of conformally equivalent shapes turned out to be a crucial cog in the proof of the Willmore conjecture.

The Rubber-Band Men

Neves and Marques' strategy for proving the Willmore conjecture is actually rather simple to explain—and very difficult to carry out. In fact, their proof is 95 pages long.

If you have traveled on a long plane flight, especially in a modern airplane that shows your progress on a video display, you may have noticed that your route does not appear straight on the map. It is called a "great circle" route. Great circles, like the equator, are minimal paths in the sphere. They pass the first-derivative test for minimizing length. There is only one way of modifying the equator that makes it shorter (sliding the whole thing north or south). If you modify it in any other way, such as by putting in a detour around the Galapagos Islands, you will always make it longer. Thus, mathematicians say that a great circle is a *critical point of index 1* for the length functional. The index tells you the number of ways to make the length shorter.

Completely analogously, the hypersphere has a 2-dimensional "equator" that is also a minimal surface of index 1. This equator is an ordinary sphere.

Now suppose you didn't know about equators. How could you find these minimal curves, or minimal surfaces, without knowing about them in advance? One method, called a "min-max" procedure, was pioneered (in the form that Marques and Neves used it) by Fred Almgren and Jon Pitts. You take a rubber band that makes a small loop around the south pole, and then slide it around the globe until it makes a small loop around the north pole. You could do this in an easy way just by sliding it along the sphere without stretching it. Or you could do it the hard way by stretching it past the equator and letting it relax again. Either of these procedures is called a *homotopy*. It should seem clear, intuitively, that the "easy way" gives no information about the overall shape of the sphere, but the "hard way" does; we'll say that it detects the sphere's topology.

Now take any homotopy and find the length of the rubber band at its longest stage. This is the "max" part of "min-max." The "min" part has to do with the fact that we're using a rubber band; we assume that it pulls itself taut at every stage of the homotopy. If your homotopy detects the topology of the sphere, the curve that results from this min-max procedure is guaranteed to be minimal. In the case of the rubber band being pulled from the south pole to the north pole, this point of maximum stretch-and-tautness occurs when it passes the equator. (See Figure 3)

Now, suppose you want to find a torus of least area in the hypersphere. Neves and Marques proposed to detect it by using the same "min-max" procedure, only using inner tubes in place of rubber bands. But it is essential to find a large enough family of inner tubes.

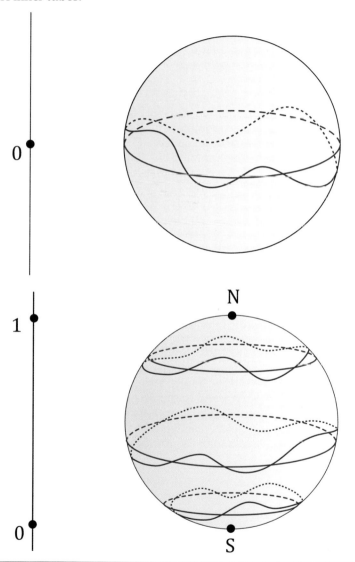

Figure 3. *The min-max procedure. A red rubber band moves from the bottom to the top of the sphere, reaching a point of maximum length around the middle. When the* maximum *length is minimized (blue) the resulting curve is an equator or "great circle," a curve on the sphere that is minimal for length. The same procedure can be applied to produce minimal (2-dimensional) surfaces in a (3-dimensional) hypersphere. (Pictures originally designed by Carlos Matheus for a blog post on Willmore's conjecture. Courtesy of Carlos Matheus Santos.)*

The proof sounds so natural that it's hard to believe no one had thought of it before—until you realize all the hard work and the geometrical and topological ideas that are necessary to show you can apply the min-max principle to *any* **canonical family.**

This is where the conformally equivalent surfaces enter the picture. Back in 1990, Francisco Urbano had shown that the Clifford torus and its family of conformal equivalents (the cyclides of Dupin) have index 5, but no other minimal torus has index smaller than 6. If you want to detect a minimal surface of index 5 with the min-max procedure, you need a five-parameter family of comparison surfaces. (By contrast, since the equator has index 1, we were able to detect it with just a one-parameter family of rubber bands.) Marques and Neves' first clever idea was to start with any surface $\tilde{S}$ in the hypersphere, look at all of its conformally equivalent surfaces (four parameters) and all their *equidistant* surfaces (that is, surfaces that are at a constant distance d from the original $\tilde{S}$ or any of its conformal equivalents). This gives a five-parameter family, as the parameter d is added to the four parameters that describe the conformally equivalent surfaces. Neves and Marques called this the "canonical family" associated with $\tilde{S}$, and asked what happens when you apply the min-max procedure to it.

First, they had to show that the canonical family actually detects the topology of the sphere. They did this by showing that the degree of the homotopy at the boundary—a measure of how many times it covers the sphere—is equal to the number of holes in the original surface $\tilde{S}$. "We were very excited when we found that out!" says Marques. It meant that if your starting surface $\tilde{S}$ is a torus, its "canonical family" must be homotopically nontrivial. Thus the min-max surface $\tilde{S}$ in this family is minimal. They also showed that it remains a torus; in other words, it is impossible for the sliding procedure to destroy the hole in the torus.

At this point, the impatient reader must be wondering what any of this has to do with the Willmore conjecture, which is about minimizing the bending energy, not the area. Remember that the bending energy and the area are symbiotically related. Intuitively, if you start with any surface $\tilde{S}$ in the hypersphere and you form its canonical family, and then move toward the min-max surface in that family, you burn up bending energy and convert it to area. But the amount of curvature "fuel" is limited. After reading a paper by Antonio Ros of Granada University, Marques and Neves realized that the area of the min-max surface is always less than the Willmore energy of the starting surface:

$$\text{Area}(S') \leq W(\tilde{S}).$$

To wrap up the Willmore conjecture, they merely had to show that

$$2\pi^2 \leq \text{Area}(S').$$

Putting these together, it follows that the Willmore energy of any torus is at least $2\pi^2$. Because the Willmore energy of the Clifford torus equals $2\pi^2$, as explained earlier, it follows that the Clifford torus has the minimum possible Willmore energy.

The missing step—the second inequality above—is surprisingly elegant. Assuming there were a minimal torus with area smaller than $2\pi^2$, Neves and Marques considered the smallest one, S_0. It would not be a Clifford torus, and hence by Urbano's theorem it would have index at least 6. Then it would be possible to perturb S_0 a little bit to get another surface, S_1, whose canonical family has a smaller maximum area. But the min-max surface in *that* family is also minimal, and has area less than S_0. This contradicts the assumption that S_0 was the smallest minimal torus. The proof sounds so natural that it's hard to believe no one had thought of it before—until you realize all the hard work and the geometrical and topological ideas that are necessary to show you can apply the min-max principle to *any* canonical family.

"In our favor, the method of min-max was largely ignored in the field for 30 years, and did not belong to the bag of standard tricks," says Neves. "We were thinking about it for different reasons, and when we realized the existence of the canonical family with so many good properties, we immediately thought of min-maxing it to prove the Willmore conjecture."

Ben Andrews. *(Photo courtesy of Ben Andrews.)*

Trying Not to Collapse

Marques and Neves' proof contains, *inter alia*, a proof that the non-spherical minimal surface of least area in the hypersphere is the Clifford torus. Scarcely a month later, Simon Brendle showed that the Clifford torus is in fact the only minimal torus without self-intersections. (This is known as an "embedded" minimal torus. Other non-embedded tori do exist.)

Brendle's approach is completely different, but it likewise uses an approach that was not in the "bag of standard tricks." The approach, called a non-collapsing principle, was discovered only very recently, through the work of Gerhard Huisken and Ben Andrews.

Huisken had given an elegant new proof of a theorem due to Matthew Grayson, which says that if you let a curve in the plane "flow" in the direction of its curvature vector, it will always round itself out to a circle before disappearing. This is a remarkable fact, because the curve can be a labyrinthine maze, and yet the walls of the labyrinth will never collapse towards each other; they always seem to know which way to go. The maze straightens itself out without any external intervention.

Huisken's approach was to define a function on pairs of points in the curve that roughly measures the ratio of the straight-line distance between the points to the distance along the curve. He then showed that the minimum value of this function is always increasing, so that it can never go to zero (which would happen if the walls of the evolving labyrinth pinched together).

Andrews extended the idea to closed surfaces, such as inner tubes, that evolve in the direction of their mean curvature. Given any point x on the surface S, imagine inflating a spherical balloon in the interior of S, the way that a doctor inflates a stent in an artery. During this process the mouth of the balloon stays fixed at x. At some point the balloon will run into the wall, so that it can't be inflated any farther without losing its spherical shape. Two things can stop it: either the part of the tube that is "infinitely close" to x or the far side of the tube, at some point y a finite distance away.

In Andrews' original paper, he compared the curvature of this balloon/stent to the mean curvature of the surface, and showed that the ratio cannot decrease to zero (which would happen if the tube were to collapse). Note that the proof could not possibly work if the mean curvature were zero, because the ratio would be undefined. For this reason, Andrews says, he never even thought of applying the same idea to minimal surfaces. But Brendle did.

Brendle came up with a much more sensitive approach that was inspired by both Huisken's and Andrews' ideas. Like Huisken, he defined a function of two variables, $Z(x, y)$, that you can think of as a stenosis detector. The function is never negative, and it equals zero only when x and y are points of maximum stenosis. Brendle's function is defined for minimal surfaces because it compares the curvature of the balloon/stent to the *maximum* principal curvature of the surface. For a minimal torus, this is never zero (a theorem proved by Lawson). He then used a "maximum principle" argument, replacing the non-collapsing argument, to show that $Z(x, y)$ cannot have a minimum value where $x \neq y$.

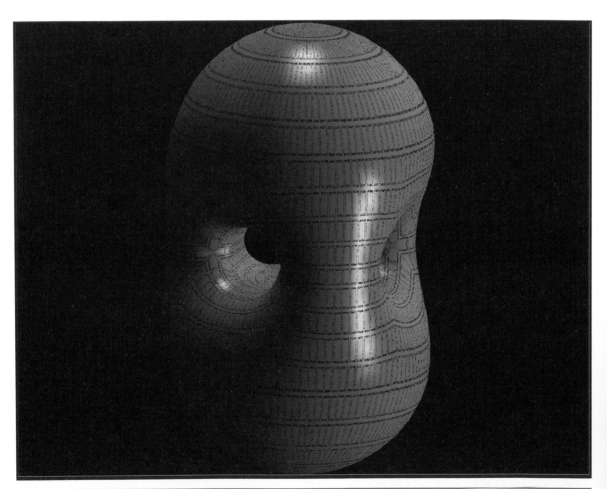

Figure 4a. *Examples of Willmore surfaces with 2 holes (Figure 4a) and 3 holes (Figure 4b). These are minimal (locally minimizing) but not necessarily globally minimizing for bending energy. Mathematicians still do not know the shape of the 2-holed or 3-holed torus with the least possible bending energy. (Figure courtesy of Dr. Ivan Sterling.)*

Thus, for a minimal torus, the largest interior ball touching any point x has curvature equal to the maximum principal curvature of S at x. And now a key point: Because S is a minimal surface, there is no real difference between the inside and the outside. (Remember that the air pressure on each side of a soap film is the same.) So the largest *exterior* ball has curvature equal to the minimum principal curvature of S at x. In other words, the surface everywhere has to thread its way between two tangent spheres whose sizes are known. This forces a great deal of rigidity on the surface. In fact, Brendle showed that the principal curvatures have to be constant, and from this he deduced that S has to be a Clifford torus. The argument involves some technical computations, but even so it is quite beautiful because it applies several classical theorems in differential geometry (the Gauss-Bonnet theorem, 1848; the Codazzi equations, 1868; the Simons formula, 1968) to the very non-classical function $Z(x, y)$.

Figure 4b. *Example of a Willmore surface with 3 holes. (Figure courtesy of Dr. Ivan Sterling.)*

So it turns out that torus-shaped soap films and soap bubbles (in the hypersphere) and torus-shaped lipid vesicles (in Euclidean space) can be pretty interesting. What's next?

After seeing Brendle's paper on the preprint archive, Andrews and his collaborator Haizhong Li of Tsinghua University (where Andrews was visiting) immediately thought of applying the same technique to constant mean curvature (CMC) or soap bubble-like surfaces (see Table 1, page 19) in the hypersphere. The main complication is that for a soap bubble, the inside *is* different from the outside; it has higher "air pressure" precisely because it's the inside. This meant that instead of being sandwiched between two tangent spheres at every point, the surface has only one spherical constraint. One might say that it's an open-faced sandwich. Even so, the lack of stenosis was a powerful constraint, and the two mathematicians managed to show that any embedded CMC torus has rotational symmetry. In fact, it is either an analogue of the Clifford torus or it is an analogue of the Delaunay surfaces in Euclidean space. Andrews and Li subsequently realized that this was a conjecture that had been proposed in 1989 (but not proved) by Ulrich Pinkall and Ivan Sterling.

However, one other fact turned up that no one had anticipated. As Brendle had showed, a CMC torus with mean curvature 0 (i.e., a minimal surface) must be a Clifford torus. Strangely, there is one other number with the same property. A CMC torus with mean curvature $1/\sqrt{3}$ likewise must be a Clifford-like torus (to be precise: a Cartesian product of two circles, which however have unequal radii). The Delaunay surfaces are not allowed.

Andrews explains this phenomenon roughly as follows. In Euclidean space, Delaunay surfaces extend to infinity, but in a sphere they have to close up again. This imposes a periodicity constraint that limits the number of possible Delaunay shapes (for any given value of the mean curvature) to a finite set. Below mean curvature $1/\sqrt{3}$, it is possible to find a CMC torus with two "undulations." Above mean curvature $1/\sqrt{3}$, a CMC torus can have three undulations. But exactly at mean curvature $1/\sqrt{3}$, these surfaces collapse. For example, the necks joining the three undulations pinch all the way down to a radius of zero. Consequently the surface is not smooth, and it cannot count as a CMC torus.

So it turns out that torus-shaped soap films and soap bubbles (in the hypersphere) and torus-shaped lipid vesicles (in Euclidean space) can be pretty interesting. What's next?

One obvious followup would be to study Willmore surfaces and minimal surfaces of more complicated topology—with two or more holes (see Figures 4a and 4b, pages 26 and 27). However, it is difficult to know even what to conjecture about these surfaces. Even if there were some conjectures with convincing numerical evidence, the existing proof techniques would be difficult to extend. For instance, to find two-holed minimal tori using the max-min technique, you would probably need an even larger family of "canonical surfaces" to compare them with, and it is far from clear how such a family could be constructed.

It is probably more likely that the *techniques* used in the proofs, such as the max-min principle and the non-collapsing principle, will enter the geometer's bag of "standard tricks" and be applied to other problems in differential geometry. What the consequences will be, nobody can predict.

Willmore died in 2005 and never got to see the proof of his conjecture. But appropriately, in March 2012, just a few days after his conjecture was proved, Durham University honored his memory with a sculpture of a Willmore surface in the shape of a torus (see Figure 5).

Figure 5. *Sculpture of a torus-shaped Willmore surface. Rendered in stone from a computer graphic, this is one of many "cruller" shapes that are minimal but not minimizing for the bending energy. The minimizing torus, which is shaped like a doughnut rather than a cruller, is shown in Figure 1. (Photo courtesy of Durham University.)*

Figure 1. *Damage in Wakuya, Japan, after the March 11, 2011 tsunami. Note seawall in foreground, which was far too short and was breached in two places. Also note the cruise boat that was deposited on top of a building (center) as the tsunami retreated, giving an idea of the height of inundation. (U.S. Navy photo by Mass Communication Specialist 3rd Class Alexander Tidd.)*

Tsunamis: Learning from Math, Learning from the Past

O N MARCH 11, 2011, AT 2:46 PM, AN EARTHQUAKE rumbled beneath the sea floor about 70 kilometers off the coast of Japan. Half an hour later, the waves started barreling into the tiny fishing town of Ryoishi, population 600.

Ryoishi was protected by an enormous seawall, whose height had recently been doubled to 9.3 meters. You might compare it to the Green Monster, the fabled 11-meter outfield fence at Fenway Park in Boston. But the Green Monster is made of wood; the wall at Ryoishi was reinforced concrete. The residents were reassured by engineers that it would protect them against any conceivable tsunami.

In a video on YouTube (http://www.youtube.com/watch?v=X6GzxcXsecg), taken from a vantage point high above the wall, you can see what happened to the engineers' predictions. At first, the incoming wave looks like a stream meandering through the center of the harbor. It doesn't look like a wave at all. Cars and trucks continue to drive by on the inland side, unperturbed by the oncoming water.

About three and a half minutes into the video, there is a subtle change. Suddenly you realize that it isn't just a stream any more. *The entire bay is moving toward the land.* As boats crash and splinter against the seawall, the water rises with stunning swiftness. Suddenly the idea of holding it back with such a puny wall seems absurd. Around the five-minute mark, the water gushes over the top and keeps on rising. After a while you can't tell that the wall was ever there.

In the end, the March 11 tsunami rose to twice the height of the hapless wall. Forty-five people, or about 7 percent of Ryoishi's population, perished. Nationwide, the death count rose to more than 15,000 people. Though it was less than one-tenth the toll of the 2004 Boxing Day Tsunami in the Indian Ocean, it was still a stunning loss of life for a country that is better prepared for tsunamis and earthquakes than any other in the world. Japan has seen so many tsunamis over the centuries that it coined the word (*tsunami* means "harbor wave" in Japanese).

The catastrophe (see Figure 1, facing page, and Figure 2, next page) underscored how much we still don't know about tsunamis (see Box, **How Tsunamis Differ from Ordinary Waves**", page 33). On "3/11," Japan was victimized by a triple whammy of events. First, the magnitude 9.0 earthquake that triggered it was larger than seismologists believed possible at that location. (In fact, it was the strongest earthquake in Japan's recorded history.) Second, the magnitude was initially reported as 7.9, enough to produce a tsunami but not a

Figure 2. *The seawall in Taro, Japan, seen here before the tsunami (top) and about three months after (bottom). Throughout northern Japan, seawalls that had supposedly been built for a worst-case scenario were not high enough to contain the Tohoku tsunami. (Photographs courtesy of H. Todd Stradford.)*

catastrophic one. Some people may have been lulled into a false sense of security by these early reports. And third, the tsunami itself—particularly along the Sanriku coast, including Ryoishi—was larger than most mathematical models can account for (even given the correct magnitude of the earthquake).

In a certain sense, the calculus of life and death during a tsunami is quite simple. People who get to high ground will live, like the videographer on YouTube. But in other ways it is not simple at all. How do you tell what is high enough? If you want to build evacuation shelters, how high should they be? Can you provide a forecast more nuanced than "A tsunami is coming"? Can you predict the height, the arrival time, or the current velocity? (Height isn't everything—a fast-moving one-meter tsunami can sweep people out to sea and do a great deal of damage (see Figure 3, page 35)). And how do you avoid false alarms? Not every offshore earthquake produces a tsunami, and false alarms can adversely affect the public's preparedness when the real thing comes along.

The answers to these questions require mathematical models. Over the last ten to twenty years, both the models and the data fed into them have improved considerably, to the point where it is reasonable to hope for tsunami forecasts with comparable accuracy to weather forecasts. Ironically, though, these gains are in danger of being lost—at least in the U.S.—because of uncertain funding for the critical infrastructure that makes the forecasts possible.

Tsunami Basics

The story of mathematical models for tsunamis begins quite a long time ago. In 1871, Adhémar Jean Claude Barré de Saint-Venant wrote down the first version of the equations that are used today in most tsunami forecasting models. Though sometimes called the Saint-Venant equations in his honor, they are more commonly called the "shallow water equations."

For a wave propagating down a narrow, shallow tube, such as a canal (the case that Saint-Venant was most interested in), the shallow water equations look like this:

$$\frac{\partial h}{\partial t} + \frac{\partial}{\partial x}(hu) = 0,$$

$$\frac{\partial}{\partial t}(hu) + \frac{\partial}{\partial x}(hu^2) + \frac{\partial}{\partial x}(gh^2/2) = -gh\frac{\partial B}{\partial x}.$$

For waves inside an ocean, which has two large and one much smaller dimension, there is a third equation that includes derivatives in the y direction.

In the above equations, the unknown functions are $h(x, t)$ (the height of the water column at location x and time t) and $u(x, t)$ (the average velocity of the water in the water column above location x and time t). The first equation expresses the conservation of mass, saying that the rate at which water is flowing into the water column at x equals the flux of mass through the sides. The second equation expresses Newton's second law. The first term is the rate at which momentum (hu) enters the water column; the second term is the flux of momentum through the sides. The third term is the spatial derivative of the hydrostatic pressure—a force term, because a difference in pressure creates a net force on the water column. The final term introduces the bathymetry, or depth of the bottom of the canal, $B(x)$. In a canal or ocean of constant depth the derivatives of B are zero and the last term disappears. However, if the depth varies, the canal bottom or seafloor can absorb momentum or reflect it back into the wave.

The shallow-water equations behave nicely as long as the amplitude of the wave is much less than the depth of the water and the depth of the water is much less than the wavelength. The latter assumption accounts for the term "shallow-water equation"—the water is shallow compared to the length of the wave. Ironically, the shallow-water equations most accurately describe a tsunami in *deep* water. The height of a tsunami seldom exceeds a meter in the open ocean, while the depth is around 4 kilometers and the wavelength is typically a hundred kilometers. (It is determined by the size of the region of seafloor uplifted by the earthquake that generates the tsunami.) Under these conditions, the shallow-water equation is nearly linear.

In the open ocean, the shallow-water equations predict that waves will travel at a velocity of $\sqrt{gh}$. For a typical tsunami,

> **The height of a tsunami seldom exceeds a meter in the open ocean, while the depth is around 4 kilometers and the wavelength is typically a hundred kilometers.**

this is about 200 meters per second, or roughly the speed of a jet. Tsunamis are fast! The velocity is independent of the wavelength, so the wave does not "disperse" or separate into smaller waves of different wavelengths.

When the tsunami gets close to shore, though, the depth B and height of the water column h decrease rapidly and the wave slows down. But the rear of the wave, which is still 100 kilometers out to sea, starts catching up to the front, which makes the amplitude of the wave grow. This is a nonlinear effect called "shoaling." Eventually the wave may break, another nonlinear effect. In addition, waves of different frequencies will disperse, with the shorter waves traveling slower, so that from above the tsunami may look like a train of smaller waves. For all of these reasons, the behavior of the tsunami near shore becomes more difficult to analyze. Pencil and paper calculations have to give way to computers. In this regime some computer models use the Boussinesq equations, which take into account the effects of dispersion as well as vertical motion of the water.

Once the wave sweeps over land, the math becomes even more formidable. The boundaries of the water start moving. The wave loses energy as it crashes into boats, buildings, trees, vehicles, and people on shore. At present, most models lump all of these items together into a single "roughness coefficient." However, the roughness can change; the buildings that resist

Figure 3. *Across the Pacific Ocean, the boat "Mona Lisa" was moored to a smashed pier in Santa Cruz harbor, the day after the main tsunami. It acted like a weathervane, pointing the direction of the current in the normally placid harbor. The current reversed direction every 15 minutes or so; each in-and-out cycle marked the passage of one tsunami wave. (Photographs courtesy of Dana Mackenzie.)*

the first wave may be obliterated by the time the second one comes along. Or, vice versa, debris from the first wave may form a dam that holds up later waves. "No one's model is very accurate once the wave goes onshore," says Harvey Segur, an applied mathematician and tsunami modeler at the University of Colorado.

Operational Models and Research Models

Different models take different approaches to the multi-scaled nature of tsunamis. The model used by the U.S. National Oceanic and Atmospheric Administration (NOAA), called SIFT (see Figure 4, next page), first reconstructs the pattern of uplift and subsidence of the seafloor from the seismometer readings from the earthquake, along with the known geology of the fault zone. SIFT assumes that the deformation of the seafloor occurs instantaneously (a not quite accurate assumption, but it does happen much faster than the speed of propagation of the water waves). It also assumes that the initial shape of the

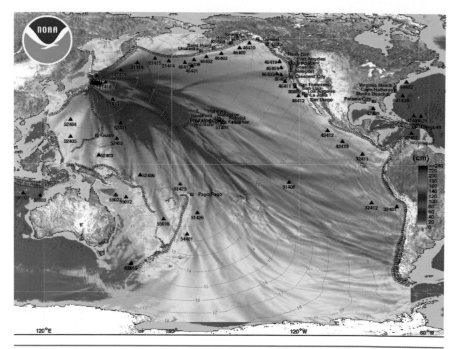

Figure 4. *Forecast of the maximum amplitude of the 2011 tsunami, generated by the SIFT model. Numbered triangles denote locations of DART buoys,
and "zippers" mark the locations of pre-computed earthquakes. The real
tsunami is modeled first as a superposition of the pre-computed ones, and
then corrected with observational data from the DART buoys. The validity
of this approach relies on the near-linearity of the shallow water equations.
(Courtesy of National Oceanic and Atmospheric Administration.)*

wave exactly reflects the change in the seafloor. For instance, in
the case of the Tohoku quake of 2011, the seafloor on the ocean
side of the fault rose by about 3 meters, while the floor on the
Japanese side subsided by $\frac{1}{2}$ to 1 meter.

As the waves propagate outward from the epicenter, they
eventually pass over buoys that the NOAA has deployed along
all the major fault zones in the Pacific Ocean. These are known
as DART buoys (short for Deep-ocean Assessment and Report-
ing of Tsunamis). Before the Indian Ocean tsunami of 2004,
only eight DART buoys had been deployed in the entire Pacific
Ocean and none in the Indian Ocean. Now there are 51 of them.

DART buoys work by sensing the pressure at the seafloor.
Even though a tsunami wave in the ocean is only a meter high, it
nevertheless increases the hydrostatic pressure at the bottom
by the weight of that one extra meter of water. The buoys can
transmit their readings to NOAA within seconds. These readings provide new data used to correct and update the original
earthquake model (see Figure 5).

The next step is an application of the near-linearity of
the shallow-water equations in deep water. NOAA has pre-
computed solutions to the full, nonlinear shallow-water equations from 1691 predetermined sources. These sources run
along the entire Pacific rim like a zipper running down the
center of a shirt. (See Figure 5.) Each of these 1691 model earthquakes has magnitude 7.5, which is considered the minimum
to create an ocean-crossing tsunami.

Of course, it is unreasonable to expect every earthquake to be confined to one source region and have magnitude exactly 7.5. However, it is possible to *linearly combine* these sources to match the true earthquake that was observed. (A perfect match may not be possible, but a simple least-squares procedure produces the best possible match.) Because the shallow-water equations are nearly linear in deep water, the very same linear combination of the corresponding tsunami waves will be a reasonably accurate forecast of the tsunami... in deep water. This method of generating a forecast is extremely fast, because it is just a matter of algebraically combining solutions that have already been computed and stored in computer memory.

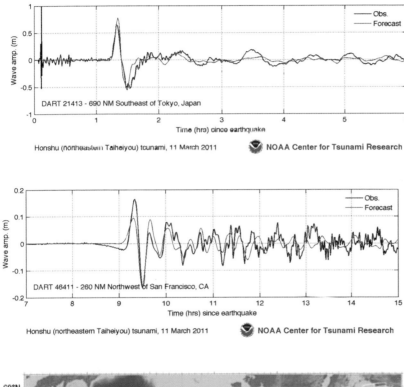

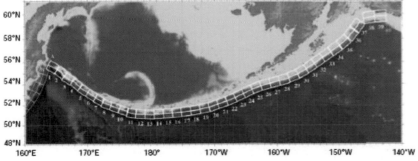

Figure 5. *Readings from two DART buoys during the 2011 event (black) compared with forecasts (red). Timing of the earliest waves is quite accurate, amplitude somewhat less accurate. The DART buoy near Tokyo (top) recorded seismic tremors in addition to water-pressure variations; newer DART buoys can tell the difference between the two. Bottom: Locations of precomputed earthquake sources for SIFT model. (Courtesy of National Oceanic and Atmospheric Administration.)*

However, in shallow water the linear combination will cease being accurate, because of the effects of nonlinearity and dispersion. Thus, for the last stage of the computation, the NOAA model takes the output of the deep-water model and inputs it to a finer grid that starts a few tens of kilometers offshore. (Actually there are two refinement stages, as the grid size is stepped down from 1 kilometer to 180 meters to 30 meters.) Fortunately, it is not necessary to develop a prediction for the entire coast—only for the major population centers. Near each of these cities, SIFT uses detailed measurements of the bathymetry (the $B(x)$ term in the shallow wave equation) to compute the local solutions in real time. In this way the model arrives at a local forecast for the tsunami height and the regions at risk for flooding.

For people near the earthquake—the people in Japan—there is scarcely time to do more than issue the first forecast based on the seismometer readings. But for people on the other side of the ocean—the people in America—the forecasts can be issued in plenty of time to take preventive action. (For instance, boats in harbor can put to sea, where they will be safer; people can be evacuated from low-lying zones; and emergency personnel can be sent where the greatest damage is likely to occur.)

The NOAA approach is not the only one. Randy LeVeque, an applied mathematician at the University of Washington, along with his student Dave George, who now works at the U.S. Geological Survey, developed a solver for the shallow water equations called Geoclaw. It uses a method called adaptive mesh refinement to drive a seamless model of the tsunami from the deep ocean up to the shore and inland. While NOAA's model changes resolution at predefined locations, the adaptive model shifts scale *when the physics says it has to*—in other words, when nonlinear effects like shoaling and breaking start showing up. In this way the model makes much more efficient use of computer resources. It is also better in other ways: instead of three layers of refinement, it has five; and it uses new approaches to grid computations, such as a procedure known as the discontinuous Galerkin method, which are better able to simulate shocks and propagate them forward.

"If you didn't use adaptive mesh refinement and had to use a static grid, our model could easily take several weeks to run," says LeVeque. "It takes us 5 to 6 hours for a full run with adaptive mesh refinement." Of course, again, this is too slow for the people of Japan, but it is fast enough to give people in California a useful forecast. LeVeque does not have the option to use precomputed solutions to speed the computation up, nor does he need to.

"The missions of the two codes are different," says LeVeque's colleague, oceanographer Frank Gonzalez. "Theirs [the NOAA's] is used for operational purposes, as opposed to research. Their purpose is to satisfy the country's need for immediate forecasts. You have an enormous infrastructure of people who keep it running 24/7." As research code, Geoclaw does not have to be up and running all the time. On the other hand, it is open-source and freely available to other academic researchers, while the SIFT code is proprietary to NOAA.

Other research groups have developed other types of models. Some, for example, use the Boussinesq equation, which is particularly appropriate if the researchers want to look at smaller-scale events such as landslide-generated tsunamis, where the wavelength is comparable to the ocean depth. Some take different approaches to modeling the initial deformation of the seafloor. Instead of idealized equations that assume a homogeneous and flat seafloor, they use finite element methods (the kind of unstructured grid used to design cars and airplanes) to better capture the complexity of the real seafloor. In addition, some codes incorporate time dynamics, instead of assuming instantaneous rupture of the Earth's surface.

Preparedness Counts

The most important thing that any community can do to prevent deaths during a tsunami is to have a good evacuation plan and be ready to use it. A paper by Eddie Bernard, the director of NOAA's Pacific Marine Environmental Laboratory, puts it succinctly: "For the Aonae, Japan case [a tsunami in 1993] about 15 percent of the population at risk died from a tsunami that struck within 10 minutes of the earthquake because the population was educated about tsunamis, evacuation plans had been developed, and a warning was issued. For the Warapa, Papua New Guinea case [in 1998] about 40 percent of the at risk population died from a tsunami that arrived within 15 minutes of the earthquake because the population was not educated, no evacuation plan was available, and no warning system existed." In the 2011 Tohoku tsunami, the combined fatality and missing rates were no more than 10 percent in even the hardest-hit communities. Although 10 percent is a staggering death toll, the difference between 10 percent and 40 percent is even more staggering.

Anecdotal accounts abound of the importance of public awareness. At the time of the 2004 Indian Ocean tsunami, Tilly Smith, a 10-year-old girl from the United Kingdom, was on vacation in Phuket, Thailand. She had just seen a video of the 1946 Hilo, Hawaii tsunami in a geography lesson at school. As her family walked along the beach on the morning of December 26, she recognized the frothy and "sizzling" appearance of the water as a tsunami precursor. Her parents did not believe her at first, but she screamed at them that they needed to get back to the hotel. On the way, her father alerted a security guard, and he spread the word to other vacationers. Thanks to Smith's geography lesson, everybody at the hotel fled the beach in time and nobody died. It was in stark contrast to the scene on other beaches in Thailand, where thousands of people died.

A much sadder story in Constitución, Chile, shows that education may not be enough in the absence of a plan. Many citizens of Constitución camp out on a low island in the mouth of the Maule River during the end-of-summer festival. "The local population has a long history of being exposed to tsunami hazard, and after ... the Indian Ocean event, they were particularly aware of how to interpret the signs of a tsunami," wrote Diego Arcas and Harvey Segur in *Philosophical Transactions of the Royal Society A*. When

---

a magnitude-8.8 earthquake struck on February 27, 2010, Arcas and Segur wrote, "Everybody on the island knew what was to come next, but, without bridges and only a couple of boats to evacuate the island, there was no possible escape for the hundreds of people who perished."

Finally, a happier story came out of the Japanese earthquake in 2011. Everybody knows about the Fukushima nuclear power plant, which suffered a cooling failure and a partial meltdown after being inundated by the tsunami. It was a different story at the Onagawa nuclear power plant, which survived a 13-meter tsunami unscathed and served as a shelter for people who lost their homes. "With all the disarray in the nuclear village of Japan, there had to be a story of someone doing something right," wrote Woody Epstein, a risk analyst for the Japanese power industry, in his blog.

Epstein gives credit to Hirai Yanosuke, a manager at the Tohoku Electric Power Company, who did not believe a 12-meter breakwater would be high enough. He eventually convinced the company to build a 14.8-meter breakwater. By contrast, the Fukushima reactor, owned by Tokyo Electric Power Company, was only designed to withstand a 5.7-meter wave. "He wasn't the sort to believe that everything would be all right as long as people fulfilled standards and procedures," Epstein blogged. Epstein also believes that the Tohoku Electric Power Company took the risks more seriously because everybody in the company lived nearby.

"We should not underestimate the importance of having local people running and managing a nuclear power facility," Epstein wrote. "The Onagawa nuclear power plant is owned by a Tohoku company located in Sendai, managed by Tohoku people, and staffed by Tohoku people."

"It reminded me of the first time I was at the NoK nuclear power plant in Beznau, Switzerland, to look at the Notstand building, a bunkered facility which could support all of the plant systems for at least 72 hours .... . I asked Martin Richner, the head of risk assessment, why Beznau spent so much money on the Notstand building when there was no regulation or government directive to do so. Martin answered me, 'Woody, we live here.'"

Although the most dramatic and urgent application of tsunami models is forecasting, they also have several other important uses. One of them is education and emergency planning—preparing for a tsunami years before it happens. Also, models can generate "what if" scenarios. In the Japanese tsunami, what if the wall at Ryoishi had been higher? What if a breakwater had not been installed at Kamaishi, which possibly deflected some of the waves to Ryoishi? What if the parameters of the 2011 event were varied—the rupture made closer to the surface, the seabed softer or firmer? And finally, models facilitate learning from the past—seeing what really happened, not only in the 2011 tsunami but also in tsunamis that took place centuries ago.

Certainly one of the lessons of 2011 was the importance of learning from the past—and not just the recent past. Tsunami modelers, including the ones who had developed hazard assessments for the Fukushima nuclear power plant, had confidently assumed that a tsunami of this size could not occur. And yet there are known deposits from a tsunami in 869 AD that was almost an identical twin to this one. A stone tablet above the village of Aneyoshi says, "High dwellings are the peace and harmony of our descendants. Remember the calamity of the great tsunamis. Do not build any homes below this point." And yet, modern people did (see Figure 6).

Another lesson, says Phillip Watts, a tsunami scientist and president of Applied Fluids Engineering in Long Beach, California, is that "There is no maximum tsunami, only less and less likely ones." The 2011 tsunami was a once-in-a-millennium event. A tsunami twice its size might occur once every 10,000 years. Because there is no maximum, it may be unreasonable to attempt to build "hard" countermeasures (seawalls, breakwaters, emergency shelters) for every conceivable case. It may make more sense to prepare hard countermeasures for a 500-year event and rely on "soft" countermeasures (education, evacuation, emergency services, insurance) to deal with anything larger.

For this reason, one of the hot areas for research right now is *probabilistic* tsunami hazard assessment, which seeks to quantify the areas at risk in a 100-year or 500-year tsunami. This is a departure from past practice, which has attempted to map out maximum inundation zones. Gonzalez, along with 20 colleagues, recently published such an assessment for Seaside, Oregon, showing that the main risks for 100-year tsunamis are Alaskan earthquakes, but the main threat for a 500-year tsunami is an earthquake in the Cascadia Subduction Zone, off the coast of Washington. (The last major earthquake there happened in 1700.) In each case the document maps out which areas of Seaside would be at risk (see Figures 7a and 7b, on pages 42 and 43).

Deconstructing the Tohoku Tsunami

In spite of all the challenges, there were some real successes for tsunami modelers amidst the devastation of the Tohoku tsunami. It was, without question, the best-monitored tsunami in history. The enormous volume of videos on YouTube attests to that. But amateur videographers were not the only ones watching. After the water retreated, researchers collected more than 5000 readings of the high-water marks along the Japanese coast.

In addition, the 2011 tsunami was one of the first major tests of the scaled-up system of DART buoys, and they performed very well indeed. In fact, the DART buoys provided the first clues that the 2011 earthquake was very much larger than the first seismometer readings suggested.

"When they issued the first estimate, 7.9, by that time we already had a signal in the closest DART," says Diego Arcas of the University of Washington, who leads the modeling group at NOAA's Center for Tsunami Research. "When we ran an inversion, our inversion indicated it had to be about an 8.8."

Unfortunately, Arcas could not do anything with that information. "In our lab we do an experimental forecast—we do not

Figure 6. *Tsunami markers in Taro, Japan, before and after the 2011 tsunami. Lower marker indicates the height of a 1933 tsunami, and the upper one shows the height of the 1896 tsunami. Seawall was built roughly to the height of the 1933 tsunami. Actual height of the 2011 tsunami was above the top of this cliff. (Photographs courtesy of H. Todd Stradford.)*

have operational responsibilities," he explains. "We did tell the tsunami warning centers that we were getting an 8.8, but nobody knew whether we were right or wrong." The more accurate seismometer readings did not come in until 3:14 pm, 28 minutes after the earthquake. At that point, Japanese authorities revised their estimates from a 3-6 meter tsunami to a 10-meter one. But for many people, that news was too little, too late.

This experience suggests that DART buoys should be placed closer to the seismic zones so that the very first forecasts can be based on both the tsunami meters and the seismic signal. Unfortunately, the first generation of DART buoys were deliberately placed a certain distance away from the known faults,

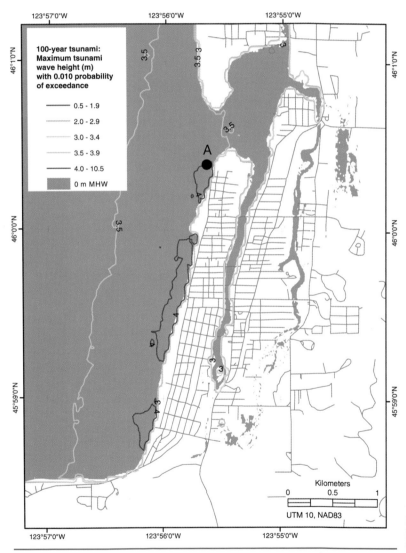

Figure 7a. *(a) Inundation map of Seaside, Oregon, for a 100-year tsunami triggered by an Alaskan earthquake. Flooding is limited to near-shore areas. (Figure reproduced by permission of American Geophysical Union. From F. Gonzalez et al., "Probabilistic tsunami hazard assessment at Seaside, Oregon, for near- and far-field seismic sources," Journal of Geophysical Research* **114**, *C11-23,* © *2009 American Geophysical Union.)*

because the data sampling rate was not high enough to distinguish seismic waves from hydrostatic pressure variations. Putting the DART buoys a few minutes' travel away allows the faster-moving seismic waves to pass by before the hydrostatic waves arrive.

However, the second generation of DART buoy, which is already in the prototype stage, does not have this limitation. These buoys could be placed right next to the faults. But the money to do this is running out. The Tsunami Warning and Education Act, which funded many of the DART buoys, expired in 2012, and the proposed 2013 budget included a $4.6 million decrease in funding for the NOAA's National Tsunami Hazard Mitigation Program. It is ironic that the money to upgrade the DART system would dry up, just at a time when the

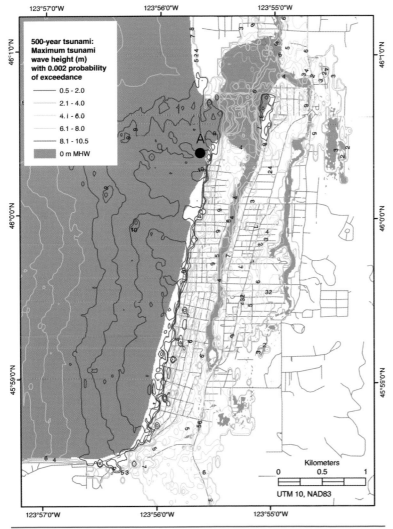

Figure 7b. *(b) Inundation map for a 500-year tsunami triggered by an earthquake in the Cascadia Subduction Zone. Most of the city is at risk for flooding. (Figure reproduced by permission of American Geophysical Union. From F. Gonzalez et al., "Probabilistic tsunami hazard assessment at Seaside, Oregon, for near- and far-field seismic sources," Journal of Geophysical Research 114, C11-23, © 2009 American Geophysical Union.)*

**"Landslide tsunamis are where the action is,"
Wells says. "They are
less frequent than
earthquake-generated
tsunamis but, aside
from the 2004 Indian
Ocean tsunami, they are
responsible for more
deaths. The Japanese
tsunami is an example."**

means exist and the Japanese experience has demonstrated a clear value in doing so. Besides the money issue, scientists and mathematicians have some other conundrums to think about. First, as Watts says, "seismologists are all atwitter" about an earthquake that basically thumbed its nose at some of their cherished beliefs. A 9.0 earthquake is not supposed to be possible in a region as compact as the Tohoku earthquake's rupture zone, which was only 480 kilometers long. All around the world, and not just off the coast of Japan, worst-case scenarios will have to be revised upward.

Then there is the matter of the tsunami that was too high. LeVeque has plugged a dozen different earthquake models into Geoclaw, and not a one of them has correctly forecast the runup heights that were actually observed on the north coast. (South of 39 degrees latitude, the models work much better.) Other modelers have reported the same problem: their computations of the tsunami wave runup along the Sanriku coast are off by a factor of as much as two (see Figure 8).

Several explanations have been offered for the discrepancy: inaccurate models of the bathymetry; "splay faults" that run perpendicular to the main fault, which may cause an uplift of the seafloor disproportionate to the magnitude of the earthquake; inaccurate models of runup in the narrow valleys that characterize the Sanriku coast; and underwater landslides triggered by the earthquake.

For Watts, an expert on underwater landslides, the explanation is clear. Everything about the tsunami that hit the northern coast—its anomalous size, its limited extent, the fact that it came in two pulses with the second much bigger than the first (which is very evident in the Ryoishi video)—suggests a landslide that was triggered after the earthquake. "It's a precise mathematical calculation," he says. "I use the Boussinesq equations, and the only way to reproduce the tsunami is to have the right chunk of land moving the right distance. From mechanical calculations of the landslide, there is only one solution that works. The model leaves nothing to chance."

Other experts, including LeVeque, are not convinced yet; they want to see a smoking gun, in the form of a fresh landslide scar on the continental shelf. But if Watts is right, the Tohoku tsunami may underscore the importance of landslide-generated tsunamis. These already came to geologists' attention once before, in 1998, when a magnitude 7.0 earthquake off Papua New Guinea was followed by an unexpectedly huge tsunami that killed 2200 people. It is generally accepted now that the earthquake triggered an underwater landslide, and the latter produced the anomalous tsunami.

"Landslide tsunamis are where the action is," Wells says. "They are less frequent than earthquake-generated tsunamis but, aside from the 2004 Indian Ocean tsunami, they are responsible for more deaths. The Japanese tsunami is an example." His data show that landslide sizes are essentially uncorrelated with the magnitude of the earthquakes that produce them, so a small quake can still produce a major landslide. You can think of it as the straw that breaks the camel's back. Wells' nightmare scenario is a smallish, magnitude 6 earthquake that just happens to generate an underwater landslide comparable to the one that (perhaps) occurred off Japan. The result would be a 20- or 30-meter tsunami that no one would see coming.

The United States got off pretty lightly from the 2011 Japanese tsunami. For most people it was a curiosity more than a threat. But it's important to realize that the same thing could happen in our back yard. The next major earthquake on the Cascadia Subduction Zone could easily do as much damage to the northwest coast, if we aren't prepared. And the possibility of a landslide tsunami also should not be ignored, even on the east coast.

"It's an unlikely disaster, maybe in the 1000- to 10,000-year range, but it's repeated all along Oregon, California, the east coast," says Wells. "It may be once in 10,000 years for southern California, but for the U.S. as a whole, it may be a 200- to 2000-year event. Suddenly that puts it in the historically relevant range."

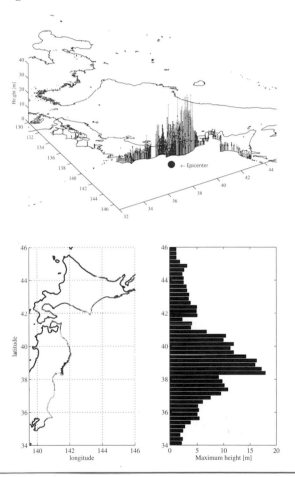

Figure 8. *(top) Observed tsunami runup heights (green) and inundation heights (red) in the 2011 Tohoku tsunami. (bottom) Modeled tsunami runup heights. Note that models severely underestimate the height of the waves north of the 39th parallel. The discrepancy has not been explained. (Figure courtesy of World Scientific Publishing Company, from N. Mori and T. Takahashi, "Nationwide Post Event Survey and Analysis of the 2011 Tohoku Earthquake Tsunami," Coastal Engineering Journal, Vol. 54, No. 1 (March 2012), © 2012.)*

"Hot Spots." *PredPol's crime prediction algorithm identifies regions (in red) where crimes are more likely to occur over the following 24 hours. The original version of the algorithm is based on an earthquake prediction method. More sophisticated versions, as shown here, incorporate geographical information to exclude certain regions where a crime is unlikely. The pictured region is the San Fernando Valley in California. Two large purple regions, where crime is unlikely, are the Van Nuys Airport (top) and the Woodley Lakes Golf Course (bottom). (Image courtesy of Martin B. Short.)*

Today's Forecast: Ten Percent Chance of Burglary

IN THE FIRST SIX MONTHS OF 2012, the Foothills division of the Los Angeles Police Department reported one quarter fewer burglaries than it had in the first six months of the previous year, and a 13 percent reduction in crime overall. Meanwhile, none of the city's other twenty divisions reported such a large drop in crime, and in fact the city as a whole had a slight increase (see Figure 1, next page).

What happened in the Foothills division that made it so unusual? Did 25 percent of the burglars move away? Did a large number of people suddenly install burglar alarms?

Neither of these explanations is correct, but the actual explanation may sound equally far-fetched. During the first half of 2012, Los Angeles was conducting an unprecedented controlled experiment to test the effectiveness of predictive policing. Every day, a mathematical model would analyze the recent patterns of crime in the Foothills division, along with historical records, to identify the most likely locations of burglaries and other property crimes in the coming day. The software generated 20 predicted "hot spots," each one roughly 150 meters by 150 meters, and police officers were instructed to pay extra attention to each of those areas. For example, when not actively engaged in responding to another call, the officers were encouraged to drive through the nearest hot spot to keep an eye on it.

To serve as a control for the experiment, the police department at the same time generated areas of interest using its standard procedures. On any given day, a computer-generated random number—in essence, a flip of the coin—would determine whether the officers on the beat would receive the computer-generated forecasts or the ones generated by human analysts. The officers themselves would not know which one they had been given.

Over the course of the experiment, the computer-generated forecasts were about twice as accurate as the human ones. The improvement was dramatic enough to convince even skeptical beat cops. At the conclusion of the experiment, the Los Angeles Police Department expanded the predictive policing program to cover five more divisions, and it plans to extend it to the rest of the city over the next year.

Though news accounts have tended to focus on the arrests made by officers patrolling the "hot spots," the police department was even more gratified to see the reduction in the overall crime rate. The goal of predictive policing, after all, is not more arrests but less crime. "We have prevented hundreds and hundreds of people coming home and seeing their homes robbed," police captain Sean Malinowski told the Associated Press.

Even before the Los Angeles experiment, the news media was agog over predictive policing. The algorithm, developed by George Mohler, a mathematician who is now at Santa Clara

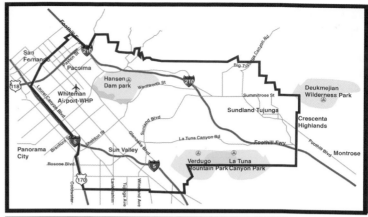

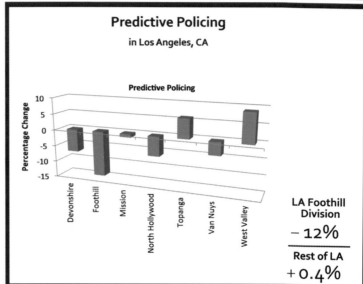

Figure 1. *(Top) Map of the Foothills Division in Los Angeles, where the Los Angeles Police Department conducted a field trial of predictive policing in the first half of 2012. (Bottom) Results of predictive policing trial, based on LAPD figures and provided by PredPol. The Foothill Division had the largest decrease in overall crime, and the rest of the city had a slight increase. For property crimes, a specific target of the PredPol model, the improvement in the Foothill Division was close to 25 percent.*

University, was first tested in 2011 by the Santa Cruz police department. After the trial began, the burglary rate in Santa Cruz dropped about 27 percent, reversing the trend that had taken place over the first six months of the year. That experiment was not conducted with a control group and therefore the change could not be attributed definitively to predictive policing. However, the circumstantial evidence was strong. In addition, news reporters from the *New York Times*, NBC and ABC rode along with police officers and watched actual arrests being made in regions that Mohler's program had identified. On the basis of such reports, *Time* magazine named predictive policing as one of the 50 leading inventions of 2011.

Law enforcement experts have also been impressed. Because of the massive interest from other law enforcement agencies,

Mohler has launched a company called PredPol to market the software. "All of these agencies want to use it, and the only way to get it to them was to start a company," he says. "I don't have the resources, because I'm just a professor who teaches calculus." As of July 2012, two more California cities, Salinas and Morgan Hill, are using the software, and PredPol has received inquiries from more than 200 others across the country.

It's safe to say that all of this was the last thing Mohler expected when he arrived as a postdoc in the mathematics department at UCLA in 2008. At the time, the soft-spoken and unpretentious Mohler was a specialist in computational fluid dynamics, with no previous experience in law enforcement or criminology. However, he was lucky enough to be joining a mathematics department that had begun a major collaboration with the LAPD a few years earlier.

The police commissioner of Los Angeles at that time, Bill Bratton, had made a name for himself in Boston and New York by introducing a technology-friendly approach to policing called CompStat. Now used in many police departments, CompStat is not predictive policing, but it was a big step towards computerizing law enforcement. "What Bratton did was to put the crimes on a map and ask the staff to be responsible for those crimes that happened in their divisions," says Jeff Brantingham, an anthropologist at UCLA. "People think that he used that as a basis for new policing strategies. But in reality, it was all very retrospective: What have you done about these crimes?"

When Bratton came to Los Angeles in 2002, Brantingham, who is the son of two well-known criminologists at Simon Fraser University, sensed that the police department would be receptive to other innovative ideas. He secured the LAPD's cooperation in sharing crime data, and then he went out looking for mathematicians who could figure out what to do with it. The first two he found were Andrea Bertozzi and Lincoln Chayes, also at UCLA.

"Mark Green [the director of the Institute for Pure and Applied Mathematics at UCLA] asked me if I wanted to talk to a young anthropologist, so we set up a luncheon," Bertozzi says. "I was a little skeptical before I met him. I was not used to talking with social scientists who have a real grasp of mathematics." But Brantingham sold her on the project; as Bertozzi says, it was a chance to work in a nearly unexplored field. "I had been working in imaging science, and this was a new problem area for me that was not already well picked over, like image processing." Along with Chayes and criminologist George Tita, Brantingham and Bertozzi received a National Science Foundation grant in 2006 to study the formation of crime "hot spots." (They were soon joined by another postdoc, Martin Short.)

In the early days, the mathematical models that the group developed were mostly theoretical. They began with stochastic agent-based models that were based on the movements of individual criminals along an idealized grid. Later, they followed this one with a deterministic differential equation model that was in essence a continuum limit of the stochastic model. These models led to theoretical insights, such as the mechanism by which new "hot spots" of crime could emerge. They could also make quantitative predictions, for example,

> Brantingham...sensed that the police department would be receptive to other innovative ideas. He secured the LAPD's cooperation in sharing crime data, and then he went out looking for mathematicians who could figure out what to do with it.

about whether increased policing would suppress crimes in a region or just displace them elsewhere. The results were published in high-profile journals such as the *Proceedings of the National Academy of Sciences*. However, these models were never intended as practical law-enforcement tools. One reason is that they depend on too many parameters (such as the mobility of criminals) that are difficult or impossible to measure in practice.

Even if the mathematicians were not yet producing results of practical significance, Brantingham says that the early years were important for building credibility and trust with the LAPD. "From the get-go, we said we wanted to understand the mechanism of hot spots, and they cooperated, recognizing that the initial results would be very theoretical in nature. We never pushed the idea that we had a silver bullet, and we have been very careful not to over-promise. The good science has been done in small, incremental steps."

When George Mohler joined the group in 2008, the time was ripe for the project to move in a more practical direction. He learned from a colleague in the statistics department about a model that geologists use to forecast earthquakes, and he suggested that the same model might very well apply to crimes as well.

Earthquakes and crimes have several things in common. First, they do not occur uniformly everywhere. Earthquakes occur with a certain "background" frequency that is higher along faults and lower in regions with no known faults. Likewise, crimes have a higher "background" frequency in certain neighborhoods than in others.

Andrea Bertozzi. *(Photo courtesy of Andrea Bertozzi.)*

George Mohler (left) with Zach Friend (right). *(Photo courtesy of Dana Mackenzie.)*

Earthquakes also have a "self-exciting" property: Large earthquakes are nearly always followed (and sometimes preceded) by a series of associated quakes. This association can be seen clearly in a histogram of the time intervals between consecutive earthquakes along a typical fault. Without the self-exciting property, the likelihood of an earthquake occurring in any particular time interval would be constant, and the histogram of time intervals between successive quakes would decline gradually according to a Poisson distribution. However, the actual distribution is very different from a Poisson distribution, with a sharp peak at the shortest time interval.

Just like earthquakes, crimes beget other crimes. In some cases they are committed by the same individual, moving on to other targets. In other cases they are copycat crimes, as other people see the opportunity. Many burglaries occur at exactly the same location as a recent previous one (see Figure 2, next page). Violent crimes can also show a high degree of clustering; for example, a gang-related murder often precipitates a series of retaliatory acts.

In seismology, the conditional intensity $\lambda(x, y, t)$ of earthquake occurrences at location (x, y) and time t is often assumed to have the following general form:

$$\lambda(x, y, t) = \mu(x, y) + \Sigma g(x - x_k, y - y_k, t - t_k).$$

In this equation, $\mu(x, y)$ is the background rate at which earthquakes occur (note that it depends on x and y, but not on t). The parameters x_k, y_k, and t_k are the coordinates and times of recent earthquakes, and the function g represents the self-excitation process. This function expresses the way in which an earthquake at (x_k, y_k, t_k) generates a heightened probability of aftershocks at nearby points and times. Of course, g decreases to zero as either the distance or the time separation goes to infinity. In addition, it is worth noting that g is a function of earthquake magnitude, because larger earthquakes are more likely to generate aftershocks.

Figure 2. *The crime prediction algorithm relies on the fact that criminals return to the same sites over and over again. Here, an abandoned church in South Bend, Indiana, shows the signs of multiple break-ins—-as well as repeated attempts by the owners to discourage them. (Photo courtesy of Keith Board.)*

Such models have been studied for years in the seismology community, and several different forms of the self-excitation term have been proposed, with parameters that seismologists can estimate on the basis of geophysical theories. But in the application to crimes, it is less clear what the specific form of g should be or what the corresponding parameters are. For that reason, Mohler made a crucial modification to the earthquake model. Instead of prescribing g in advance, he allowed the data to determine the most likely excitation function. This was accomplished by an iterative procedure. At each step and for each pair of crimes i and j, he calculated a probability p_{ij} that event i was an offspring of event j, as well as the probability p_{ii} that event i was self-generated (i.e., a background event).

He would then use these probabilities to sample the existing database of event pairs. From this sample he would infer the shape of $\mu(x, y)$ and $g(x, y, t)$, using a procedure called kernel density estimation. Then he would recompute the probabilities p_{ii} and p_{ij} and go to the next round of iteration. To validate the procedure, he conducted simulations with a known self-excitation function and compared them with the iteratively computed function. In these simulations, 75 iterations were enough to give a fairly good match between the inferred g and the actual one.

Mohler made a few other tweaks to the earthquake model. He allowed the background crime rate to depend on time, so that it could, for example, change according to the weather or reflect weekly patterns of behavior. (For instance, burglaries might happen more often on weekdays, while homeowners are at work.) He also omitted the terms related to the intensity of the precipitating event. Earthquakes come with magnitudes, but the same is not necessarily true of crimes. In any case, we do not have any standard measure of the "magnitude" of a crime that would correspond to the magnitude of an earthquake.

Next Mohler tried applying his algorithm to historical data from 2005, provided by the LAPD. He found that the modified earthquake algorithm could predict about 20 percent more burglaries than a previously published crime model that does not separate crimes into background and offspring events. Although that may seem like a fairly modest improvement, Brantingham notes that it was achieved in spite of a kernel density estimation procedure that is "horribly inaccurate." In the original algorithm, the shape function $g(x, y, t)$ is represented as a sum of Gaussian functions (bell-shaped curves), and the resulting hotspot map looks like a very blurry, out-of-focus set of blobs. The team has since improved the algorithm by using kernel functions that are more sensitive to geographical features. For instance, crime has a hard time jumping over a highway, and burglaries very seldom occur in the middle of a lake (see figure, **"Hot Spots,"** page 46.).

Mohler says that the first version of the algorithm, which was published in the *Journal of the American Statistical Association*, emphasized very general, non-parametric methods to compute $g(x, y, t)$ on the advice of referees. "They are theoretically nice because they make no prior assumptions, but they over-smooth the data. Crime is very localized. One hundred meters away, you may be in an area where you can't have a residential burglary," he says. They have had better results with parametric models along the lines of those used by seismologists. In addition, the *JASA* paper noted the possibility of improving the predictive ability of the model by incorporating other types of data, such as housing density, which might allow for a better estimation of the background rate of crime.

By 2011, when Mohler left UCLA for a permanent position at Santa Clara University, he was ready to put his algorithm to a field test. At the same time, Zach Friend, a crime analyst for the Santa Cruz Police Department, saw an article in the *Los Angeles Times* about the UCLA group's work and contacted Mohler. It was a perfect match. Says Bertozzi, "They were very enthusiastic, and he saw that he could make a big impact. Also, because it's a smaller police department, there was less red tape." Santa

> ...Mohler tried applying his algorithm to historical data from 2005, provided by the LAPD. He found that the modified earthquake algorithm could predict about 20 percent more burglaries than a previously published crime model that does not separate crimes into background and offspring events.

Cruz was too small for a controlled trial, but the experiment did give Mohler a chance to improve the user interface and see how the program would fit into the workflow of an actual police department (see Figure 3).

Friend especially praises the nimbleness of the predictive policing program. He ran it once a day at 4:00 pm, and it would typically take ten minutes. The input data, he says, "could be as fresh as 3:59." By comparison, cities that use CompStat typically have planning meetings once a week, giving them much less ability to respond to trends in real time. Friend also says that it was not hard to get buy-in from officers. Six people were arrested in computer-identified hotspot locations in the first two months. "That's a tangible result for a police officer, and there are no negative results," Friend says.

Actually, some critics have noted one negative possibility. In the news media, predictive policing has been compared to the science fiction movie and story *Minority Report*, in which a department of "pre-crime" arrested people before they could commit their crimes. The crimes were predicted, in the story, by a panel of three people with precognitive powers (and the title refers to cases when one "precog" disagreed with the other two). But even leaving aside Philip K. Dick's dystopian fable, legal experts have pointed out that predictive policing could violate Fourth Amendment protections against unreasonable search and seizure.

Not surprisingly, Brantingham and the others strongly resist the comparison to *Minority Report*. Their model makes no use of individual data and, by its nature, it says nothing about *who* is likely to commit a crime. It says only where and when. In addition, unlike the science fiction story, it does not involve any supernatural powers, and it deals in probabilities rather than certainties.

Mohler has continued to refine the model and develop other approaches for different kinds of public problems. PredPol is currently planning a pilot study in San Jose of a method for predicting traffic accidents. The earthquake model is not relevant at all to traffic accidents, which have different kinds of hotspots. Nevertheless, the same vocabulary of point processes and modeling of random events can be applied.

Mohler is reluctant to discuss any details of these new projects, or to disclose the improvements that have been made to the PredPol algorithm since its initial publication. He is in a position somewhat similar to the inventors of Google, who published their basic PageRank algorithm as students but have been necessarily much quieter since then about the methods used to improve it. "We didn't have in mind that we were going to do anything like this [starting a company]," he says. "It's been a headache ever since with the intellectual property, sorting out what is in the public domain."

However, he continues, "We're constantly testing the algorithm and refining it as we learn more. There's a good analogue in finance. The Black-Scholes formula in the 1970s was a major breakthrough, but it has been refined and explored for decades. Now each financial firm has its own unique algorithm. Similarly, there is no reason to stop at our model, because it's not the best one you can come up with."

> Friend especially praises the nimbleness of the predictive policing program. He ran it once a day at 4:00 pm, and it would typically take ten minutes. The input data, he says, "could be as fresh as 3:59." By comparison, cities that use CompStat typically have planning meetings once a week, giving them much less ability to respond to trends in real time.

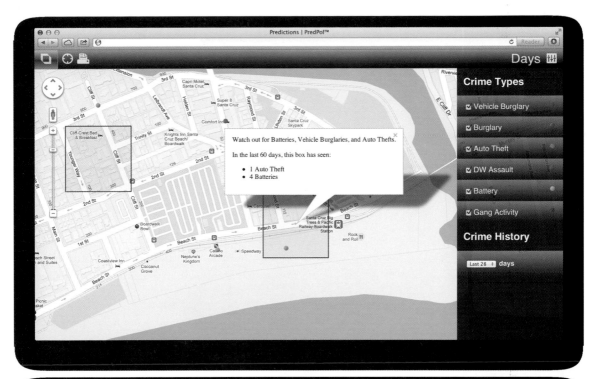

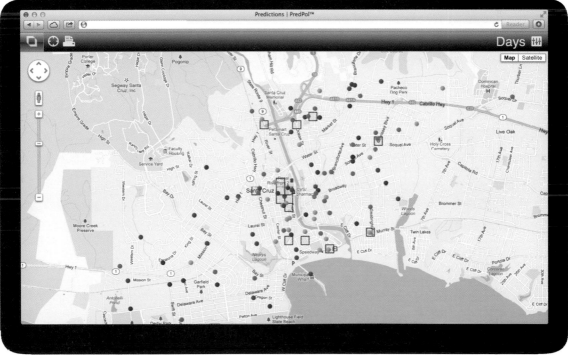

Figure 3. *Output of crime prediction algorithm—map and details. Two illustrations of PredPol's output. At bottom, an overview of the city of Santa Cruz, California, showing locations of recent crimes (colored dots, with colors indicating type of crime) and the ten most likely hot spots for today's crime (small yellow boxes). Top, zoomed-in version, shows a police officer two of the hot spots with the type of crime to watch for and information on recent criminal activity in that spot. Although the algorithm generates more "blobby" hot spots, as seen on p. 46, Mohler has found that police officers can better interpret this type of output. (Images courtesy of Zach Friend/Santa Cruz Police Department.)*

"Day & Night in Hyperbolic Space". *A crocheted art work by Daina Taimina, entitled "Day & Night in Hyperbolic Space," illustrates hyperbolic geometry. Taimina creates hyperbolic (negatively curved) surfaces by adding extra stitches at a uniform rate as she crochets successive rows. Hyperbolic spaces play a dominant role in three-dimensional topology, and a recent suite of theorems has made their structure much easier to understand. (Photo courtesy of Daina Taimina, from* Crocheting Adventures with the Hyperbolic Planes, *A.K. Peters, 2009.)*

Topologists Cross Four off "Bucket List"

I N 1982, WILLIAM THURSTON PUBLISHED AN ARTICLE in the *Bulletin of the American Mathematical Society* that foreshadowed most of the landmark developments in 3-dimensional topology over the next three decades. Thurston started the article with a conjecture:

"CONJECTURE 1.1. *The interior of every compact 3-manifold has a canonical decomposition into pieces which have geometric structures.*"

This became known as the Geometrization Conjecture, a problem that motivated the study of three-dimensional spaces for more than 20 years, until 2003, when Grigory Perelman proved the conjecture was correct. (See "First of Seven Millennium Problems Nears Completion," *What's Happening in the Mathematical Sciences*, Vol. 6.) Though Thurston was unable to prove the conjecture himself, the idea that 3-dimensional spaces have natural homogeneous geometries utterly transformed the subject of low-dimensional topology. It was akin to the way that the periodic table transformed chemistry.

But that wasn't the only thing the article became famous for. Thurston concluded with a set of 24 open problems for the future, including the Geometrization Conjecture as problem 1. For topologists, it became a "bucket list" of comparable stature to David Hilbert's famous list of 23 open problems for all of mathematics in 1900. Appropriately enough, the bucket list was very nearly completed in the final months before Thurston's death in August 2012, as four of the five remaining conjectures were proved in March.

The most famous of the four, called the Virtual Haken Conjecture, was proposed by Friedhelm Waldhausen in 1968, and it was widely considered the most important unsolved problem in low-dimensional topology after the Geometrization Conjecture. Another of the four problems, called the Virtual Fibering Conjecture, had originally seemed to be a much more ambitious version of the Virtual Haken Conjecture. Yet Thurston wrote in 1982, "This dubious-sounding question seems to have a definite chance for a positive answer."

By 2012, the gap had narrowed to the point that topologists knew that a proof of the Virtual Haken Conjecture would automatically prove the other three, including Virtual Fibering. Nevertheless, the skepticism still remained. "It [the Virtual Fibering Conjecture] is such a remarkable conjecture that it's difficult to believe it's true," wrote topologist Henry Wilton of University College London on March 6, 2012 in a blog called "Low Dimensional Topology." Less than a week later, on March 12, Ian Agol of the University of California at Berkeley announced that he had a proof. "For the suspicious, I did not know about this when I blogged last week," wrote Wilton sheepishly in his next post.

"What Agol did was really brilliant," says David Gabai, a former student of Thurston who is now the chair of the mathematics department at Princeton University. "But it was the final

William P. Thurston. *(Photo is from the Archives of the Mathematisches Forschungsinstitut Oberwolfach; and courtesy of George M. Bergman.)*

piece of a huge project. In particular, [Daniel] Wise developed this fantastic theory about subgroup separability, literally by hand with various collaborators over a period of fifteen to seventeen years. He understood the whole picture. And Agol used a crucial theorem from [Jeremy] Kahn and [Vladimir] Markovic, and [Michah] Sageev also played an essential role." In the end, it took a whole team to get to the top of the mountain.

Geometrization

Three-dimensional topologists study objects that are at once very familiar and very foreign. They are called 3-dimensional manifolds, but what they really are is spaces, just like the space we live in (omitting the dimension of time). Although they look just like our space on a small scale, they can connect up in different ways on a large scale.

For an analogy, you can connect up a strip of paper in two different ways. The "normal" way gives you a cylinder, but if you give it a half-twist before you glue the ends together, you get a Mobius strip. There is no way to tell the difference between these two surfaces on a small scale; only by looking at the surface as a whole (for example, by counting the number of sides) can you tell the difference.

Topologists have developed many tools for telling spaces apart. One of the most powerful and the most basic is called the fundamental group. If M is a manifold, its fundamental group, denoted $\pi_1(M)$, records all the different ways that you can draw a loop in the manifold. The loops are allowed to move around, so that it might be better to call them lassos. Figure 1 shows a two-dimensional manifold, called a torus or T^2, with four

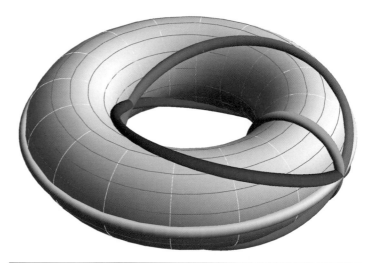

Figure 1. *Four different elements of the fundamental group of the torus. Each loop corresponds to a pair of numbers, representing the number of times the loop winds around the torus longitudinally and how many times it winds "latitudinally." For example, if +1 corresponds to going around counterclockwise and −1 corresponds to clockwise, the green curve would correspond to the pair $(0, 1)$, the orange would correspond to $(1, 1)$ and the red to $(1, -1)$. (Image by Stan Wagon, Mathematica in Action, Springer 2010.)*

different lassos drawn on it. There is no way to tighten any of these lassos down to a point, because they all get hung up in one way or another on a neck of the torus. Furthermore, none of them can be maneuvered smoothly into the position occupied by one of the other lassos. Thus they represent distinct and nonzero elements of the fundamental group. It is possible, in fact, to create lassos that circle the torus in either the short way or the long way two, three, or any integer number of times. Thus any element of the fundamental group corresponds to a pair of integers (p, q), with p indicating how many times the lasso wraps around the torus in one direction, while q denotes how many times it wraps around in the other. Topologists express the result as follows: $\pi_1(T^2) = Z \oplus Z$, where the two Z's (short for the German word *Zahlen*, or "numbers") denote the group of integers.

Ian Agol. *(Photo courtesy of Stefan Friedl.)*

The fundamental group is a powerful tool for classifying manifolds, and in fact for two-dimensional surfaces it is the only tool that you need. Considering only orientable (two-sided) surfaces for simplicity, the only possibilities are a sphere, a torus, a two-holed torus, and so on. Each one of these spaces has a different fundamental group.

One reason that the fundamental group is so useful is that it is *algebraic*. For example, in the case of the torus it reduces to pairs of numbers. Algebra enables you to do topology symbolically and, for example, calculate the properties of your manifold on a computer. Indeed, at some points in the proof of the Virtual Haken Conjecture it is not completely obvious whether you are doing geometric topology or geometric group theory. Agol's and Wise's solution abstracts away the three-dimensional and topological origins of the problem, working with fundamental groups instead.

In addition to their algebraic structure, given by the fundamental group, two- and three-dimensional manifolds also have a *geometric* structure, and the geometry interacts in a wonderful and complicated way with the algebra.

To understand the meaning of a geometric structure on a 3-manifold, it might help to think about beams of light in space. A manifold with positive curvature is one in which beams of light tend to focus, because of the curvature of space. A real-world example is the focusing of light beams from distant stars as they pass by our sun. This focusing creates a "gravitational lens," and its detection in 1919 was probably the most important single piece of evidence behind Einstein's theory of general relativity. Einstein's equations had predicted that a massive object like the sun should create a region of positively curved space around it.

The prototypical example of a space with positive curvature is the sphere. Notice that if two people start traveling in two different directions from the north pole, and travel south in the "straightest possible" path (called a geodesic), their paths will converge again at the south pole. This is another example of the focusing property of positively curved space.

Flat space is also easy to understand; it has the geometry we learn about in high school. In a manifold with zero curvature, the width of a light beam stays constant. The prototypical example is an infinite, flat tabletop. Another example, less obvious, is the Clifford torus (see "Tubing Through Hyperspace," page 16). Although a torus or inner tube in three-dimensional space is nonuniform, with some regions of positive curvature and some regions of negative curvature, by inserting the torus into four dimensions it is possible to iron the whole thing flat.

Negative curvature is somewhat more elusive, but it is crucial to three-dimensional topology because most spaces are negatively curved. In a space with negative curvature, light beams tend to spread out—not because they bounce off of dust (the usual reason for the spreading of light beams in our atmosphere), but because of the curvature of space itself. (See Figure 2.) The prototypical example of a space with negative curvature is called the *hyperbolic plane*, a non-Euclidean geometry discovered in the nineteenth century by Nikolai Lobachevski, Karl Friedrich Gauss and Janos Bolyai. In the twentieth century, M. C. Escher made it familiar to millions through his art work.

Figure 2. *A distinctive feature of hyperbolic geometry is that nearby geodesics (curves that are the straightest possible paths within the surface) tend to spread out. In this crocheted model by Daina Taimina, the two yellow geodesics are close to each other in the center but much farther apart (measuring along the red surface) by the time they reach the edge. (Figure courtesy of Daina Taimina.)*

The last ingredient in geometrization is uniformity. Topological manifolds are "born" without any particular geometry; like a sheet of rubber, they are free to bend and stretch in any conceivable way. But Thurston realized that the global structure of a 3-manifold typically allows it only one uniform geometry (i.e., one with the same curvature at every point). That geometry makes the space rigid, and can be used to identify the space just as the fundamental group can.

Among two-dimensional spaces, the sphere has a uniform positively curved geometry; the torus has a uniform geometry with zero curvature, as in the Clifford torus; and *every other* closed surface has a uniform geometry with negative curvature. The two-holed torus, for example, can be constructed in a pretty way by sewing up pieces of the hyperbolic plane.

Until Bill Thurston came along, nobody suspected that a similar statement was true about 3-dimensional manifolds. "Before Bill, it was just extremely isolated examples," says Gabai. "There were a couple examples in the early 1920s of closed hyperbolic manifolds, and Albert Marden started introducing some ideas of hyperbolic geometry in the 1960s. But Bill came in and first showed that this was part of a vast phenomenon."

From 1976 to 1977, Thurston proved that certain three-dimensional spaces, called *Haken manifolds*, have a uniform hyperbolic geometry. His students called it the "monster theorem," and it was never formally published in a journal. A generation of topologists learned about his proof from a typed manuscript of "Thurston's notes" that used to be distributed informally by the Princeton mathematics department.

Daniel Wise. *(Photo courtesy of Yael Halevi-Wise.)*

Based on this far-reaching theorem, Thurston made the even more far-reaching Geometrization Conjecture, which says that *every* three-dimensional manifold (Haken or not) can be cut into pieces, each of which has one of eight uniform geometries. The situation is thus a little more complicated than in two dimensions, where no disassembly is required and where there are only three uniform geometries (spherical, flat, and hyperbolic). However, it is possible to rephrase the Geometrization Conjecture as a trichotomy like the two-dimensional case: a three-dimensional manifold either has a finite fundamental group and spherical geometry, or its fundamental group contains $Z \oplus Z$ and it has one of six other uniform geometries, or it has hyperbolic geometry. The conjecture itself does not say anything about the fundamental group in this third case, but the work of Wise and Agol completed in 2012 gives a great deal of information about it, as we shall see.

Hakenization?

If geometrization occupied center stage from 1982 to 2003, one might say that "Hakenization" (not a real word) has been the focus of attention since then.

The term "Haken manifold" was coined by Waldhausen, in honor of Wolfgang Haken, a pioneer of three-dimensional topology. Haken's idea was to simplify a three-dimensional manifold by making cuts, analogously to the way that the two-holed torus of Figure 3 (next page) is simplified to an octagon by making strategic cuts. When you cut open a surface, the edge is a one-dimensional curve, and if the cut is a closed loop it has to be a circle. However, when you cut open a three-dimensional space, the edge is a two-dimensional surface. That surface can be a sphere or a torus or something more complicated.

Haken's program starts out by making all the spherical cuts possible and gluing spherical caps over the cuts. This will decompose any 3-manifold into simpler, "irreducible" pieces. However, you aren't done yet; irreducible manifolds come in too great a variety to provide a useful "periodic table" for 3-manifolds. The next step is to make all the torus-shaped cuts that you can. Eventually, Haken showed, you can cut your manifold up all the way into pieces that are topologically equivalent to a three-dimensional ball. Then you can reverse the process: If you want to prove a theorem about three-manifolds, you prove it inductively by adding one piece at a time. This is, in fact, exactly how Thurston proved his "monster theorem."

But there is one catch, and it's a big one. How do you know that there are any "essential tori" along which you can cut your 3-manifold open? The answer is that you don't. After the first cut you can always find places to make the remaining cuts, so if you can *start* decomposing the manifold into pieces you can always finish the job. But for most 3-manifolds you can't even get started, and these are non-Haken.

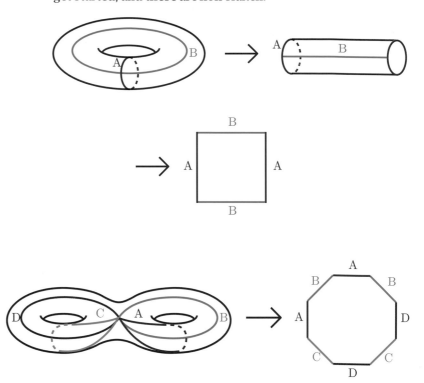

Figure 3. *Two-dimensional manifolds, or surfaces, can be simplified by cutting along essential loops, representing nonzero elements of the fundamental group. (Top) Cutting a torus along two loops, A and B, makes it possible to unroll the torus into a square. (Bottom) Cutting a two-holed torus along four essential loops (A, B, C, D) makes it possible to unfold it into an octagon. (Figure courtesy of the SimonsFoundation.org, from "Getting into Shape," by Erica Klarreich.)*

How can you deal with non-Haken manifolds? Waldhausen offered a conjecture in 1968 that was based mostly on wishful thinking: Maybe you could find a finite cover[1] that is Haken. If so, your non-Haken manifold might inherit the nice properties of the Haken manifold that covers it. In such a case, the manifold is said to be "virtually Haken." Waldhausen conjectured that all 3-manifolds that are "aspherical" (a condition that disqualifies reducible manifolds and manifolds with spherical geometry) are virtually Haken.

---

[1]Finite covers are a method often used by topologists to get rid of "bad" properties. For example, the nonorientability of the Mobius strip could be seen as a pathology. But it is possible to wrap a normal, orientable ribbon around a Mobius strip so that it covers the Mobius strip twice. This wrapping is called a double cover. In general, an *n*-fold covering will cover every point in the base space *n* times.

Waldhausen's conjecture was "in retrospect, based on reasons that are just wrong," says Nathan Dunfield, a topologist at the University of Illinois at Urbana-Champaign. Nevertheless, in one of the ironies of history, the conjecture has turned out to be correct.

At first the evidence was not encouraging. For example, out of the 246 "simplest" hyperbolic manifolds, only 15 are Haken. With so few Haken manifolds to choose from, it started to seem unlikely that every non-Haken manifold could be covered by one of them.

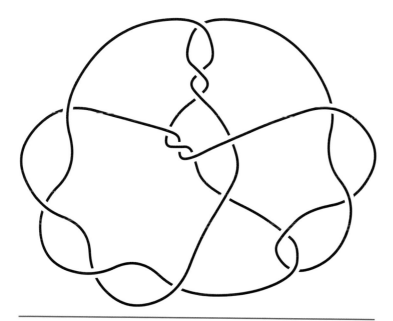

Figure 4. *In Dunfield and Thurston's census, the trickiest 3-manifold was a "branched double-cover" of the complement of this knot. Note that the 3-manifold consists of the ambient space around the knot, not the knot itself. The Dunfield-Thurston example is not Haken, but has roughly a 100,000-fold covering space that is Haken. According to the Virtual Haken Conjecture, such a covering space must exist. (Figure courtesy of Nathan M. Dunfeld.)*

However, in 2003 a computer survey by Dunfield and Thurston started to make the conjecture look more plausible again. In a census of the 10,986 simplest hyperbolic 3-manifolds, they found that every one was virtually Haken. In most cases the coverings were quite small, but in one case they had to cover the manifold more than 100,000 times before an essential torus appeared (see Figure 4)! "If the conjecture had been false, we would have just kept looking forever," Dunfield says. Instead it took them a few months.

Cubulation!

Although Dunfield and Thurston's census turned up some interesting patterns, it didn't really give any idea of how to prove the Virtual Haken Conjecture. However, a number of ideas began to coalesce around the same time, and by 2009 the activity had really heated up.

First, Perelman's proof of the Geometrization Conjecture in 2003 blew away a large chunk of the problem, because the Virtual Haken Conjecture was already known to be true for five of the six aspherical geometries. However, it remained unresolved for the last and most important case, hyperbolic geometry. Ironically, the Virtual Haken Conjecture had long been seen as a potential tool for proving the (seemingly more difficult) Geometrization Conjecture; but now the roles were reversed!

Meanwhile, Daniel Wise (now at McGill University) had been plugging away for years on an approach to the problem that few topologists thought had any chance to succeed. His approach is called "cubulation."

Wise began working on the Virtual Haken Conjecture when he was still a graduate student at Princeton in the early 1990s. His approach from the beginning was to create a discrete model of the 3-manifold by gluing squares together. (See Figure 5 for an example.)

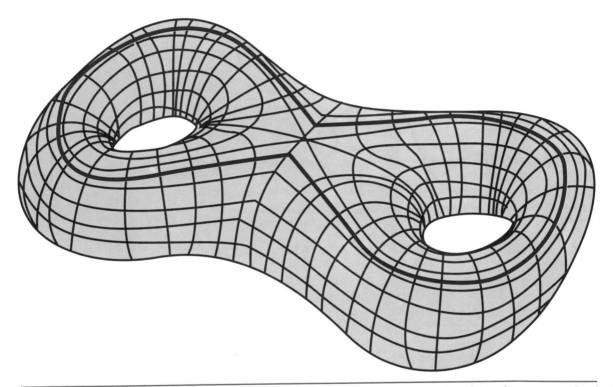

Figure 5. *A cubulation of a 2-holed torus. Wise's approach to the Virtual Haken Theorem involved the creation of discrete models called cubulations, stitched together out of squares and cubes and hypercubes. The red curve is called a hyperplane, and it is a candidate for an essential submanifold (along which the 2-holed torus can be cut to form simpler pieces). Although Wise began with simple 2-dimensional pictures like this one, the proof of the Virtual Haken Theorem requires the use of cubulations with many more dimensions. (Drawn from a diagram provided by Daniel Wise.)*

Wise's models were essentially a quilt sewn from square blocks, but with one significant difference. In an ordinary quilt, four squares touch at every corner. But in these quilts, some corners would have five or more squares sewn together as seen at the central vertex of Figure 5. This causes the quilt to pucker, and in fact it is a discrete version of negative curvature (which is exactly what Wise wanted in a model of a hyperbolic manifold).

Square complexes—and in higher dimensions, cube complexes—turned out to be a useful model because they have many, many immersed surfaces, called *hyperplanes*. To make a hyperplane, you start with a single block in your quilt, and draw a line across it, from one side to the other, dividing the block in half. When this line gets to the edge of the block, it encounters another block sewn on the other side. Inside that block, there will be a unique line that "continues" the one you have already drawn. In this fashion you keep on adding line segments, one block at a time, until you've used up all the blocks in your quilt. The hyperplane is then the sewed-together union of all the linear pieces. (It is called a "hyperplane" rather than a "hyperline" because the same construction can be done for "quilts" made of three-dimensional cubes, four-dimensional hypercubes, and so on.)

As you go through the above process of extending the complex one block at a time, you might on occasion find yourself coming back to the original block, but entering through a different side. In that case your hyperplane will cross itself. This self-intersection can be seen as a failure of your manifold to be Haken (because essential surfaces in a Haken manifold are not allowed to intersect themselves).

A cube complex is a good place to start thinking about the Haken conjecture, because it is a discrete, combinatorial object and it takes away the "floppiness" of the manifold. "When you have an immersed surface in a 3-manifold it's hard to get your hands on it," says Agol about Wise's idea. "The complex is a way of crystallizing the space of homotopies of surfaces."

The next big step forward was to free the problem from its topological origins and derive a cube complex representing M directly from the fundamental group $\pi_1(M)$ itself. To do this, you need to understand what kinds of groups *might* be fundamental groups of hyperbolic 3-manifolds. Mikhail Gromov gave a useful description of such groups using only the language of group theory; they are sometimes called "word-hyperbolic." For such groups, Michah Sageev, in his Ph.D. dissertation of 1995, showed how to construct a cubulation.

Sageev's cube complexes were more abstract than the ones Wise had been working with. They could have any number of dimensions, not just two. In a sense, the groups don't "care" about the origin of the problem in three-dimensional topology. After talking with Sageev, Wise came to realize the far-from-obvious fact that the extra dimensions actually served a purpose. In 2005, they enabled him and his collaborator Frederic Haglund to prove a highly unexpected result about what they called "special" cube complexes. "All of these special cube complexes, which we invented because they had nice residual properties [i.e., nice finite covers], naturally lived inside right-angled Artin groups," he says. "I remember the moment we discovered it as if it were yesterday. For a little while we didn't believe what we were doing, because it seemed too good to be true!"

You can think of special cube complexes as complexes that are just a little bit better than Haken. Not only are self-intersections of the hyperplanes forbidden (as in a Haken manifold), but so are two other pathologies: "self-osculation"

> **A cube complex is a good place to start thinking about the Haken conjecture, because it is a discrete, combinatorial object and it takes away the "floppiness" of the manifold. "When you have an immersed surface in a 3-manifold it's hard to get your hands on it," says Agol about Wise's idea. "The complex is a way of crystallizing the space of homotopies of surfaces."**

(when a hyperplane comes around and just touches itself—something that only makes sense in a cube complex with negative curvature) and "inter-osculation" (when two hyperplanes both intersect and osculate; see Figure 6). With these two very mild extra conditions, Wise and Haglund showed that the fundamental group of a special cube complex has an extra-special kind of group, a subgroup of a right-angled Artin group, as its fundamental group. This had all sorts of attractive and unexpected consequences. For example, the group can be represented as a group of matrices with integer entries. This result goes far beyond the virtual Haken Theorem. It shows that the fundamental group of a special cube complex is not some bizarre type of group that only experts would know about, but a familiar type of group that is seen in any undergraduate linear algebra class.

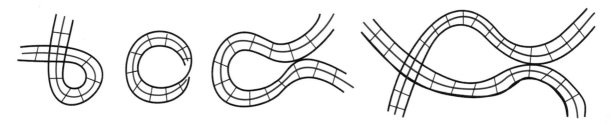

Figure 6. *Some of the pathologies that must be avoided in Wise's definition of "special" cube complexes, from left to right: A hyperplane that intersects itself; the cube complex is not orientable; a hyperplane that self-osculates; and two hyperplanes that "inter-osculate" (i.e., both intersect and osculate). If none of these pathologies occur, the cubulation has a Haken finite cover with a "fibered" structure. The second property, called the Virtual Fibering Conjecture, was once seen as highly unlikely to be true for all hyperbolic manifolds. Topologists now know that it is. (Drawn from a diagram provided by Daniel Wise.)*

Best of all, as Ian Agol showed in 2008, a 3-manifold whose cubulation is special has a finite cover that *fibers over a circle*. This sounds technical but it isn't. It reaches back to the very early days of 3-dimensional topology. Probably the easiest way to construct a 3-dimensional manifold is to take the Cartesian product of a 2-dimensional manifold with a circle. This is analogous to the way a cylinder is defined. The second-simplest way is to give the 2-dimensional manifold a twist. In other words, take the Cartesian product of the 2-manifold with a line segment (creating a "top" and "bottom" copy of the manifold), then twist the top copy any way you please, then glue the top and bottom together. It is exactly analogous to the way you create a Mobius strip.

Over the last 50 years, topologists have discovered many other fancy ways to construct 3-manifolds. The Virtual Fibering Conjecture, if it were true, would say that you can forget about all of them. As long as you are working with hyperbolic manifolds, you can construct all of them (up to finite covers) in the second-simplest way, by gluing 2-manifolds together with a twist.

This perhaps explains why the Virtual Fibering Conjecture was seen as implausible right up until a week before the end. It just seemed too good to be true. In addition, Wise and Haglund's argument *assumes* right from the start that you have a complex that is virtually Haken (plus a little bit more). In other words, it shows that *after* you have climbed Mount Everest, you can then hang-glide to the top of any other mountain of your choice. However, it does not tell you how to climb Everest.

That was the job that Agol finished up in 2012. Wise's decade and a half of work actually contained abundant clues about how to climb Everest, many of which Agol used in his proof. Apropos of this analogy, Wise comments, "I was an explorer with the goal of climbing a mountain. I made much progress on an exhaustive climb, and navigated through many obstacles and false passes and rested at a pre-summit camp contemplating the final part of the ascent. Another explorer then followed the path I had traced upwards and reached the summit first."

Agol himself is quick to acknowledge his debt to Wise, as well as to Jeremy Kahn and Vladimir Markovic, who provided a very important technical ingredient in 2009. To summarize briefly a very dense argument, here is Agol's strategy for producing a Haken finite covering of a hyperbolic manifold M. First, he produces an *infinite* covering $\tilde{M}$ in which one of the intersecting hyperplanes lifts to a nonintersecting hyperplane. Kahn and Markovic's theorem implies that there are actually *many* such surfaces; in fact, there are so many of these Kahn-Markovic surfaces inside the infinite cover that they form the "shadows" of the hyperplanes inside a higher-dimensional cube complex X. So $\tilde{M}$ contains a somewhat wobbly (because the Kahn-Markovic surfaces are not quite flat) image of what the cube complex should look like. (This idea came from a paper by Wise and Nicolas Bergeron.) From this image, plus a rather elaborate induction argument, Agol creates a finite covering of M by what he calls "reverse engineering." The spirit of the argument is that the hyperplanes of X, being of one lower dimension than X, can be assumed to have nice finite covers, and this information, plus the information on how the cells of the cube complex connect up, can be used to construct a finite covering of M within $\tilde{M}$. This covering continues to have a nonintersecting hyperplane, plus the other two ingredients required for a "special" cube complex. Thus M is not only virtually Haken, it is a little bit better than virtually Haken, and so the other results—the Virtual Fibering Conjecture and the fact that the fundamental group consists of integer matrices—follow as well.

There are two ways of viewing the landmark theorems of Agol and Wise. One way is to say that hyperbolic manifolds are as simple as we could possibly hope, in fact simpler than many topologists had dared to believe. A second, and contrarian, viewpoint is to say that finite covers are actually more versatile than we had realized. Topologists had assumed that showing a manifold was virtually Haken was the next best thing to showing it was Haken. While that is undoubtedly true, the theorems make it clear that there is a lot of structure concealed within that word "virtual." It's like saying that a seed is a virtual flower. "The results make me think that hyperbolic 3-manifolds are like a Jack-in-the-box," wrote Stefan Friedl of the University of Köln on mathoverflow.net. "When you press a button (i.e., go to an appropriate finite cover), the 3-manifold suddenly becomes a grand object of beauty... This analogy also works with a tiny seed and a bit of water, a blooming flower, etc., for the botanically minded."

> There are two ways of viewing the landmark theorems of Agol and Wise. One way is to say that hyperbolic manifolds are as simple as we could possibly hope, in fact simpler than many topologists had dared to believe. A second, and contrarian, viewpoint is to say that finite covers are actually more versatile than we had realized.

"CubeStormer II". *This Rubik's cube-solving robot, made from Lego Mindstorms pieces and equipped with a Samsung smartphone, was the first robotic solver to beat the human world record. Its unofficial best time is 4.762 seconds. Roughly 1 second is devoted to photographing the cube with the smartphone, 0.1 seconds are spent computing a near-optimal solution, and the remaining time is spent executing the pre-planned moves. (Robot design by Mike Dobson, software by David Gilday, photo by Mike Dobson.)*

Mathematicians Do the Twist

THIRTY YEARS AFTER THE RUBIK'S CUBE first twisted and turned its way into the world's consciousness, it continues to fascinate children and mathematicians alike. It has sold 350 million legal units, plus an unknown number of illegal imitations. It weathered a period of declining interest in the 1990s and a recession in the 2000s, and now it seems to be more popular and more "cool" than ever. The *New York Times* reported that Rubik's cube sales increased fivefold in the year 2008 alone.

Many people are happy even to solve Rubik's cube once. "Speedcubers," on the other hand, are so proficient that they have turned the art of solving it into a competitive sport (see Figure 1 and the Box **Speedcubing, Anyone?**, page 74), and achieved mind-bogglingly fast times. (The new world record, set in 2011, is 5.66 seconds—and it will probably be beaten in a year or two.) Others have built robots that can solve Rubik's cube. In 2011, the robots surpassed the humans for the first time, solving it in 5.10 seconds.

But for mathematicians—who might be called "slowcubers" by comparison—the most tantalizing problem of all took three decades to solve. If you were omniscient, what is the maximum number of moves it would ever take you to solve the cube? In 2010, the answer was finally revealed: "God's number" is 20.

Figure 1. *Lucas Garron, president of the Stanford Cube Club, solves Rubik's cube at a competition. The photos give an idea of the speed of the competition as well as the ways that speedcubers save precious fractions of a second. (Right) Modern cubes have smooth actions that make it possible to twirl a face with one finger. (Left) Garron throws the cube down and stops the clock. This will count as a valid solution even though one face is slightly askew. (Photos courtesy of Dana Mackenzie.)*

That, of course, is only the answer for the original, 3-by-3-by-3 Rubik's cube. To date, no one knows God's number for any of the larger cubes. (For the 4-by-4-by-4 it is somewhere between 32 and 68 moves.) However, mathematicians have shown that you can solve n-by-n-by-n cubes in a number of moves proportional to $n^2 / \log n$. Because there are $6n^2$ squares on the surface of the cube, the solutions surprisingly get more and more efficient on a per-square basis as n grows. "You can kill $\log n$ birds with one stone," says Erik Demaine of MIT.

It turns out that the strategies for solving the same cube differ in subtle ways, depending on whether you are a human speedcuber, a human with plenty of time on your hands, a robot, or "God." Perhaps the most remarkable thing about Rubik's cube is that, after thirty years, the best-selling puzzle of all time continues to offer distinct and exciting challenges to all of these groups.

Figure 2. *Some of the Rubik's cubes (and a few non-cubes) in Erik Demaine's personal collection. (Photo courtesy of Dominick Reuter.)*

Rubik's Basics

For any readers who have somehow missed it, a Rubik's cube (or *kubik Rubik* in Russian) is a plastic toy that looks like a stack of 27 smaller cubes, known universally as "cubies." In reality, a complicated mechanism inside allows any one of the cube's layers to be rotated, independently of the others. The outside of the cubies are decorated with colorful stickers, and when the cube comes out of the package all nine squares on each face have the same color.

The mischief comes when you start turning the faces. In the process, some of the colored squares are rotated from one face to another (see Figure 3). Unless you are extraordinarily careful (and no virgin cuber is *ever* careful enough), within a very few turns you will not remember how to restore the starting position. And that's when the puzzle begins.

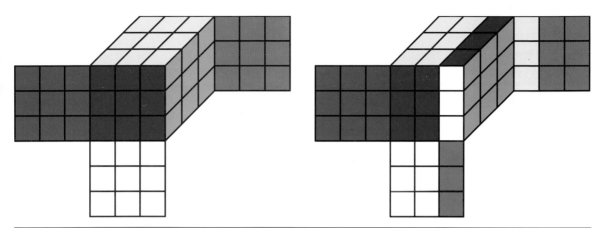

Figure 3. *Exploded view of Rubik's cube in solved state and after one turn of right face. (Figure courtesy of Tomas Rokicki.)*

The Rubik's cube provides possibly the most familiar and yet most complicated everyday example of the mathematical concept called an abstract group. It may be possible to solve the puzzle without knowing group theory, but the language of groups is by far the most convenient way to talk about it.

If you set the cube in a fixed position, at each step there are 18 possible moves. These moves are known as U (a quarter clockwise rotation of the "up" face), R, L, F, B, and D (for "right," "left," "front," "back," and "down"). Each of these six operations has an inverse (a quarter counterclockwise turn, usually denoted U', R', etc.). In addition, any face can be given a half-turn (e.g., U^2), which most cubers consider to be a *single* move, although in group theory it would normally be considered a product of two elements (U and U again). Each possible configuration of the cube can then be represented by a sequence of these letters, called a "word" in group theory.

For example, at the 2011 world championships, Michal Pleskowicz of Poland was given a cube that had been scrambled by the 19 moves B' F^2 D^2 F D' F D^2 U' B R^2 D B^2 F^2 L B' R^2 F' R F'. (All competitors receive cubes that have been scrambled in the same way, to make the competition fair.) He managed to unscramble it in 48 moves and 8.41 seconds, while his leading competitor, world record holder Feliks Zemdegs of Australia, took a disastrous 66 moves and 11.55 seconds to do so. In terms of group theory, the product of the 19 given moves and Pleskowicz's 48 moves is a 67-letter word that simplifies to the identity *I* (i.e., no move at all).

One of the earliest discoveries about Rubik's cube was the *order* of Rubik's group—in other words, the number of possible rearrangements. First, note that corner cubies always go to corners, and edge cubies always go to edges. So a naive assumption might be that any permutation of the corner cubies is possible (8! permutations), and furthermore each of the eight corners can be rotated in one of three possible ways (3^8 rotations). Likewise, there are 12! permutations of the side cubies, and each side cubie has two orientations. The "cheater's group" generated by all of these possibilities contains $8! \cdot 12! \cdot 2^{12} \cdot 3^8$ elements. This is the number of positions you can reach if you are allowed to disassemble the cube and reassemble it, or take the colored stickers off any cubie and re-paste them on the same cubie in the same cyclic order.

However, Rubik's group is not the entire "cheater's group." There are three constraints that any legal configuration must satisfy. First, the permutations of the corner and side cubies are either both even or both odd; this reduces the order of the group by a factor of 2. Second, the number of side cubies in the "wrong" orientation is always even; this reduces the order by another factor of 2. Finally, and most interestingly, if you add all the rotations of the corner cubies (which are either 0-degree or 120-degree rotations) you get a multiple of 360 degrees. This reduces the order by a factor of 3. Thus Rubik's group contains $(1/12) \cdot 8! \cdot 12! \cdot 2^{12} \cdot 3^8$, or about 43 quintillion configurations.

Ironically, the original packaging of the Rubik's cube, back in 1980, mentioned "billions" of configurations—it should have said billions of billions! However, the really substantive information is the *index* of Rubik's group (i.e., how much smaller it is than the "cheater's group"). As explained above, that number is 12.

Finding God's Number

The order of Rubik's group leads to a quick and dirty lower bound for God's number. Remember that every legal configuration corresponds to a "word" whose letters are single moves. Just by counting the number of 17-letter words (and taking into account the symmetries of the cube) you can see that there are not enough words to give all 43 quintillion configurations. So there must be some configurations that take 18 moves to solve.

In 1981, knot theorist Morwen Thistlethwaite devised an algorithm that can solve any position in *at most* 52 moves. Thus, as of 1981, God's number was known to be between 18 and 52. Thistlethwaite identified three subgroups of Rubik's group that correspond to better and better partial solutions. The group G_1 consists of positions that can be solved without doing any quarter-turns of the top or bottom faces. The next, G_2, also does not allow any quarter-turns of the left or right faces. The third, G_3, does not allow any quarter-turns at all. He showed that you can reduce any configuration to G_1 in 7 moves, from G_1 to G_2 in 13 moves, from G_2 to G_3 in 15 moves, and from G_3 to a solution in 17 moves, for a total of at most 52.

If you want to write a computer program to solve the cube, it is important to realize that Thistlethwaite's algorithm works with the *coset spaces*, G_i/G_{i+1}, instead of the whole Rubik's group. In each step except the last, you are allowed to "forget" about some of the color information on the stickers. For instance, to solve Rubik's cube "modulo G_2," imagine restickering the cube as shown in Figure 4 (top). Notice that all the yellow stickers are turned white; some blue stickers turn gray while others turn green; etc. It is important to realize that every

Figure 4. *Understanding cosets of Thistlethwaite's group* G_2 *by restickering.* Top: *The restickered version of Rubik's cube in its default state.* Middle: *Rotation of the restickered cube by one move,* R. Bottom: *A configuration of Rubik's cube that lies in the coset* $R(G_2)$. *Any configuration in this coset will, after restickering, look like the cube in the middle picture. Alternatively, any configuration in this coset will, after applying the inverse move* R', *lie in* G_2. *Thistlethwaite's algorithm reduces any scrambled cube to progressively smaller groups: Scrambled* $\rightarrow$ G_1 $\rightarrow$ G_2 $\rightarrow$ G_3 $\rightarrow$ *Solved. (Figure courtesy of Tomas Rokicki.)*

cubie in Rubik's cube has a home position, and that position determines how each of its faces should be restickered.

Now, suppose you are given a scrambled position, such as the one on the bottom of Figure 4. Find the home position for each cubie, and let that information tell you how to resticker the individual faces. The middle of Figure 4 shows the correctly restickered cube. Now observe that only one R' turn is needed to restore this restickered cube to the default position. This means one R' turn will solve the scrambled cube "modulo G_2." Or to say it differently, if you apply one R' turn to the cube at the bottom of Figure 4, you will get a configuration that is guaranteed to be in G_2. Of course, this is an unusually easy example, because it took only one turn to get to G_2. However, in general, the same principle will always apply. The same sequence of moves that solves the restickered cube will also reduce the scrambled cube to a configuration in G_2.

Speedcubing, Anyone?

One of the most surprising developments in the Rubik world over the past decade has been the emergence of a large and active speedcubing community, which has grown to include humans and robots alike. In 2011, the World Cube Association (WCA) sanctioned 300 tournaments worldwide and counted nearly 16,000 members.

For two decades after the initial Rubik's fad died out, the unofficial queen of cubing was Jessica Fridrich of SUNY Binghamton, who developed a system that she said could routinely solve the cube in 17 seconds. For the "second generation" that began cubing around 2000, 17 seconds was like the Mount Everest of cubing. At the first World Championship in 2003, Dan Knights of the University of Colorado won by averaging 20.00 seconds on five cubes. (Fridrich was second with 20.48.)

In the years since then, the world record has improved at a startling rate. In 2007, the 10-second barrier was broken. In 2008, the record dropped to 7.08 seconds. In 2010, 6.77 seconds. And in 2011, at the Melbourne Open, 15-year-old Feliks Zemdegs set the new standard at a scarcely believable 5.66 seconds. On an average of five cubes, Zemdegs' best is 7.64 seconds.

What has made the difference? First of all, today's cubes are better. Anyone who bought a Rubik's cube back in the 1980s remembers how sticky they were; each move had to be executed with a turn of the wrist. Now you only need to flick a finger to spin a face, and cubers have developed "fingertricks" that allow them to do two moves at once.

Also, the talent pool is greater, and enhanced by social media. Nowadays, all the world is a stage. As soon as Zemdegs set his record, the video was up on YouTube for everyone to see... and try to beat. And algorithms continue to improve. Fridrich's method required the cuber to memorize 57 sub-algorithms for solving the last face. Newer techniques involve less memorization; they may also try to maximize the number of fingertricks and

"R" and "U" moves, which are easier for right-handers. A few speedcubers have experimented with strategies different from the traditional "CFOP" (Cross-First two layers-Orientation-Permutation) shown in Figure 5, next page. From a total-moves standpoint, CFOP is quite inefficient, because it involves constantly breaking and restoring the first two layers.

Even more spectacular improvements have been made in robot Rubik solvers. In 2011, CubeStormer II, a LEGO MINDSTORMS robot equipped with a Samsung smartphone (which both photographs the cube and calculates a solution) improved the Guinness world record for robots by a factor of more than ten, from 64 seconds to 5.270. Its current best time (not submitted for an official world record) is 4.762 seconds.

The CubeStormer II (see Figure, **"CubeStormer II,"** page 68) designed by David Gilday and Mike Dobson, starts by photographing all six faces of the cube. This takes about 1 second, because the cube has to be rotated into position for the smartphone to see each face. The next stage, which takes 0.1 to 0.2 seconds, is calculating the actual solution. Gilday developed his own novel algorithm, which finds every way to solve a $3 \times 2 \times 2$ block in 7 moves, and from there looks in a table to see if the resulting position can be solved in 11 moves. If not, it goes to the next 7-move starting sequence and tries again. If it cannot find an 18-move solution in this way, it tries each of the 18 possible first moves and looks for an 18-move solution of the resulting position, and so on. "For almost every cube this will give us a solution in 21 to 23 moves," Gilday says.

Finally, for the last 4 seconds or so, the machine executes the pre-planned motions. Although it has the advantage of four hands, it actually twists the cube more slowly than a human. Its advantage lies entirely in the algorithm: It makes less than half as many moves as the best human speedcubers.

Gilday, an engineer at ARM (the company that designed the microprocessor inside the Samsung smartphone), has also built robot solvers for cubes up to and including $7 \times 7 \times 7$. He says that his and Dobson's future plans depend in part on the competition: "If somebody else beats our record, that would be more motivation for us to consider going farther." In the hyper-competitive world of speedcubing, you can just about count on it.

Though important for theory, Thistlethwaite's algorithm has never been very useful for human solvers, because it is difficult to tell visually that any progress is being made. Also, the original algorithm would require vast amounts of memorization. (However, in recent years, speedcubers looking for an edge have in fact devised some "human Thistlethwaite algorithms," with moderate success.)

Two major steps forward in the computation of God's number took place in the 1990s. In 1995, Michael Reid proved that

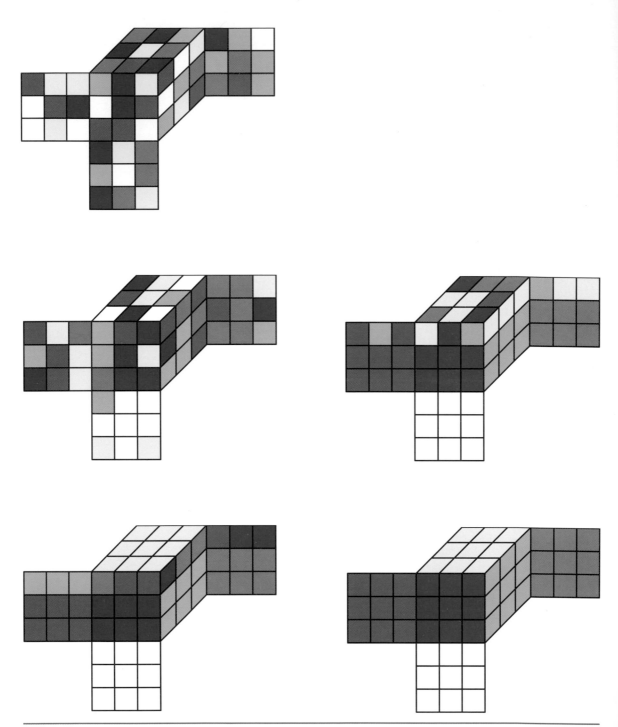

Figure 5. *A typical human algorithm for solving Rubik's cube, called CFOP.* Top: *Scrambled cube.* First stage: *Solver creates a white cross in the bottom layer.* Second stage: *Solver places the first two rows in correct positions.* Third stage: *Solver orients all the remaining pieces correctly.* Final stage: *Solver permutes all the remaining pieces correctly, and the puzzle is solved. Note that the stages in this solution all depend on visual patterns, which are destroyed and restored multiple times. The CFOP solution is far from optimal. (Figure courtesy of Tomas Rokicki.)*

a position called "superflip" requires 20 moves to solve (see Figure 6). This position, ironically, is visually quite close to a solved cube: it is the position where all of the corner cubies are in the right places with the right orientations, and all the side cubies are in the right places but with the wrong orientations. Reid's result implied that God's number is at least 20; it was the last time that the lower bound was ever increased.

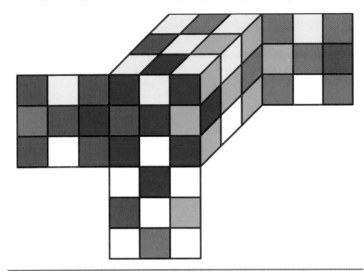

Figure 6. *"Superflip" position that requires 20 moves to solve. There is no position that requires more than 20 moves. (Figure courtesy of Tomas Rokicki.)*

Second, in 1997, computer scientist Richard Korf programmed the first *optimal* solver, which can find the shortest possible solution to any individual configuration. Korf's method applied a "depth-first" search that goes through each possible move sequence, starting with the 1-move sequences, then the 2-move ones, and so forth. It also uses "pruning tables" to abort sequences that aren't getting closer to a solution.

Using 1990s computers, Korf could solve random positions in a day. Thanks to improvements in hardware, optimal solvers can now do it in three seconds on a fast PC. Even so, because there are so many possible configurations, it would still take longer than the age of the universe to solve all of them!

Thus even after Korf's method was discovered, the problem of finding God's number still seemed hopelessly out of reach. "Almost everyone said it was impossible, at least with current technology," says Tomas Rokicki, a computer scientist in Palo Alto. "I love problems that are impossible."

Along with a varying group of colleagues, Rokicki gradually brought the upper estimate of God's number down with a sequence of ever more difficult calculations—starting out in 2008 by showing God's number was at most 25, then 23, then 22, and finally (in July 2010) reaching the finish line of 20. His proof had two main ideas that led to a more than billion-fold improvement over simply applying Korf's algorithm to every possible position. They could be called the near-optimal trick and the coset trick.

Rokicki's near-optimal trick is based on the idea that you aren't looking for the best solution for any given position;

Tomas Rokicki. *(Photo courtesy of Tomas Rokicki.)*

you're just looking for a solution in 20 moves or less. These are plentiful enough that they can be found by the following improved version of Thistlethwaite's algorithm (published by Herbert Kociemba). First you tabulate the length of the optimal solutions of all the positions in G_2 (a table of 20 billion numbers—feasible by the standards of today's computers). To estimate the number of moves to solve a given position A, you first do a depth-first search for words that get you from A to a configuration in G_2. Most of the time you will hit a configuration that takes too many moves to solve optimally. For example, you can typically get to G_2 within 9 moves; but if you are unlucky you may hit a configuration that takes as many as 18 more moves to finish, giving you a total of 27 moves. That is not very good!

However, if you take a slower route to G_2, you can often overwhelm your bad luck with sheer numbers. Rokicki says that there are typically 300,000 ways to get to G_2 with 13 moves. At least one of the resulting positions can usually be solved in 7 moves or less. Putting the two pieces together gives you a near-optimal solution. This idea alone leads to an algorithm that is 10,000 times faster than an optimal solver.

But a far greater speedup came from a second idea, which was to use the group structure to solve *billions* of positions at the same time. As Rokicki wrote, "Kociemba's algorithm motors through millions of sequences per second, but it discards the vast majority of them." That is because it is an algorithm designed to solve one particular input position.

What Rokicki realized was that you should *not* discard your misses, because they give you information about how to solve positions *related* to A. Suppose you find a sequence of (say) 9 moves that takes you from A to G_2. In other words, you found a 9-move solution to the "restickered" problem described above. It almost certainly doesn't solve configuration A. However, it *does* solve some configuration B that has the same "restickering" as A did. In the language of group theory, B and A lie in the same coset of G_2. If you think of Rubik's group as a phone book (with 2 billion pages and 20 billion names on each page!), B and A lie on the same page of the phone book.

So just by looking for short routes from A to G_2 (first 9 moves, then 10, then 11, and so on), you will find yourself filling in, one by one, the solutions to *all* the positions on the same page of the phone book as A. Suppose the optimal solution for A has, say, 18 moves. Then, in not much more time than it takes you to solve A, you can find all the positions on the same page that can be solved in 18 moves. (You may have to work a little bit harder to get the uncommon 19-move positions and the ultra-rare 20-move positions.) Repeat this 2 billion times (i.e., once for each page), and you will either have a proof that God's number is 20, or else you will find a page that contains a 21-move position.

The combination of these two tricks reduced the estimated solution time on a fast PC from the age of the universe to the lifetime of a human. By other tricks, Rokicki reduced the time by an additional 60 percent, down to 35 years. His collaborator John Dethridge, who works at Google, arranged for the requisite amount of computer time on the servers there, and the computation was completed in July 2010. No positions turned up that require 21 moves to solve. God's number was officially revealed to be 20.

Parallelizing the Cube

For 4-by-4-by-4 and larger Rubik's cubes, the problem of finding God's number is still in its infancy—about where the 3-by-3-by-3 problem was in 1981. However, in 2011 a team of five researchers led by Erik Demaine (and including Demaine's father Martin, an artist in residence at MIT) proved a surprisingly good estimate that applies to *all* sizes. As n increases, God's number for the n-by-n-by-n cube approaches a constant times $n^2/\log n$. The constant is unknown (and probably always

From left to right, Sarah Eisenstat, Martin Demaine, Erik Demaine, and Andrew Winslow. *(Photo courtesy of Dominic Reuter.)*

Anna Lubiw. *The fifth member of Demaine's collaboration. (Photo courtesy of Anna Lubiw.)*

The most remarkable thing about this result is not the constant. This result lies in a branch of mathematics called computational complexity, in which constants do not matter very much. This is quite different from the solution of individual problems, where constants may matter a lot.

will be unknown, except to God), but it lies between 12.9 and 16,777,215. (For the technically minded, we should clarify here that the definition of a "single move" is a rotation of *any* layer. This is in distinction to the 3-by-3-by-3 cube, where all moves are conventionally done with the outer layers. Also, the logarithm is to the base 2.)

The most remarkable thing about this result is not the constant. This result lies in a branch of mathematics called computational complexity, in which constants do not matter very much. This is quite different from the solution of individual problems, where constants may matter a lot. For instance, in the case of the 3-by-3-by-3 Rubik's cube, a constant was the difference between waiting a lifetime for the solution and waiting a year. But for the n-by-n-by-n cube the most important part of the result is the log n term, which, for large enough n, will outweigh any constant.

If you take a straightforward "geographic" approach to the problem, putting one cubie at a time into the proper place, it will take you a constant times n^2 moves to solve the cube, because there are a constant times n^2 cubies at the cube's surface. So among other things, Demaine's result guarantees that for a large enough cube, geographic algorithms cannot be the most efficient solution.

Demaine's team used two main ideas to speed up the solution. First, they realized that the puzzle in a sense gets easier as n increases. This is very counterintuitive, but the point is that in a large cube, most cubies are *not* edge cubes or corner cubes. You could call them interior cubies. Each interior cubie has only one colored sticker on it. This means that as soon as you get it to the correct face, you are happy with it. It will not mess up any adjacent faces. Only the corner and edge cubies need special attention and more complicated move sequences. "In the 3-by-3-by-3 case it's all special cases, which for me is more annoying," Demaine says.

Each interior cubie can go to only 24 places on the whole cube, and Demaine calls these places a cluster. Each cluster can be solved by a sequence of moves that doesn't affect any other cluster. The second key observation is that it is possible to solve many (to be precise, $\frac{1}{2}$ log n) clusters *simultaneously* (see Figure 7) with the same set of moves. It is this parallelization of the solution algorithm that accounts for the speedup for large cubes.

Why can you solve many clusters simultaneously? Look at a ($\frac{1}{2}$ log n)-by-n subrectangle of one face (in other words, $\frac{1}{2}$ log n rows). Assuming for simplicity that the cube has only 2 colors, red and blue, there are only $2^{1/2\log n}$ or $\sqrt{n}$ different patterns of colors for the columns of this subrectangle: red-red-red-..., blue-red-red-..., red-blue-red-..., and so on. This means that, on average, each of the $\sqrt{n}$ patterns will be repeated $\sqrt{n}$ times. You will thus get $\sqrt{n}$ submatrices (not necessarily consisting of adjacent columns), each of which is $\frac{1}{2}$ log n by $\sqrt{n}$ in size, in which each column looks identical. The cubes in any one submatrix can then be brought to the solved configuration (red-red-red-...) using the same sequence of moves, and without affecting any of the other clusters. When you do this for all $\sqrt{n}$ submatrices and add up the total number of moves, you find that the number is roughly $n^2/\log n$.

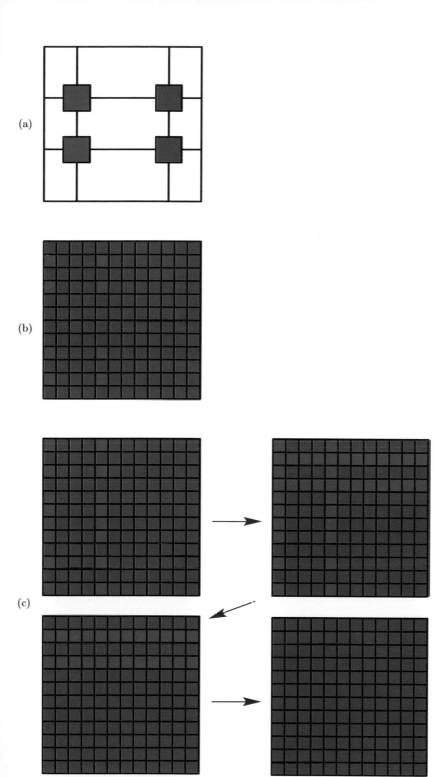

Figure 7. *Parallelizing the $n \times n \times n$ cube. Here, for simplicity, Demaine et al. consider a $1 \times n \times n$ "cube" with a red front and a blue back. (a) A typical "cluster," shown here in a state with two blues and two reds. (b) A position with four clusters in the same state. (c) Solving all four clusters with the same sequence of moves. (First, two parallel column flips; then two parallel row flips; then two parallel column flips; then two parallel row flips.) (Figure courtesy of Erik Demaine.)*

Demaine is a rare breed of crossover mathematician: a theoretical computer scientist who also admits to a love of puzzles and regularly uses them to inspire his research.

The same rough argument works when the cube has 6 colors, but the larger number of colors dramatically increases the number of possible ways a cluster might be decorated. It becomes correspondingly harder to find clusters that can be solved with the same sequence of moves. This is one reason that the rather large and unwieldy constant 16,777,215 appears in the upper bound.

The argument does not work, however, for edge and corner cubies because they cannot be manipulated without affecting other clusters. However, they can be solved using recipes imported from the 3-by-3-by-3 cube. The important thing is that these recipes do *not* have to be repeated n^2 times. They only have to be applied 8 times for the corners, and $12n$ times for the sides. Thus these special cases do not significantly slow down the performance of the algorithm.

The above argument gives $n^2/\log n$ as an *upper* bound for God's number, but surprisingly it is a lower bound as well (ignoring constants). A rough explanation, again assuming a cube with only 2 colors and again ignoring constants, goes as follows. There are roughly 2^{n^2} possible colorings of the cube. In any given position, there are roughly n possible moves. Thus the number of sequences of $n^2/\log n$ moves is about $n^{n^2/\log n}$, and with a little high-school algebra you can see that this equals 2^{n^2}. So $n^2/\log n$ is just the right number of moves to make the space of all possible words roughly the same size as the space of configurations. With fewer moves, you could not hope to reach every configuration.

Puzzles and Metapuzzles

Demaine is a rare breed of crossover mathematician: a theoretical computer scientist who also admits to a love of puzzles and regularly uses them to inspire his research. Name a puzzle and he has probably worked on it. For instance, he and his collaborators have shown that the game of Tetris with foreknowledge (i.e., you are told in advance what pieces will come next), on a board with n columns, is NP-complete. In other words, it is computationally difficult to tell whether you can survive indefinitely from an arbitrary starting position. Demaine has also shown that n-by-n sliding block puzzles, such as the popular game Rush Hour, are hard in the same sense. On the other hand, sliding-coin puzzles on an n-by-n board are computationally easy. They lie in a class of problems called P, meaning that they are solvable in a time expressible as a polynomial in n.

All of Demaine's theoretical results are really about what he calls "metapuzzles": that is, a class of puzzles with a size parameter (n) that grows larger and larger. From the point of view of computational complexity, it is meaningless to call a single puzzle (or a single instance of a puzzle) either easy or hard. Either it is solvable in finite time, or it isn't.

Instead, easiness or hardness refers to *classes* of a problem. An easy problem class has solutions that scale well, so that large instances can reasonably be solved on a computer. A hard problem class (such as the infamous Traveling Salesman Problem) does not scale well; large instances become computationally intractable very rapidly, and they *remain* intractable even if your computers get better.

The size parameter in one sense makes metapuzzles less realistic, because no one will ever play with a million-by-million-by-million Rubik's cube or play a Tetris game with a billion columns. But on the other hand, you need the size parameter to make statements like "Tetris is hard" have a permanent meaning, independent from Moore's Law.

Demaine says that he enjoys both puzzles and the metapuzzles they inspire. "With a physical puzzle, I get the same satisfaction I get from solving a math problem, where you know the professor already has a solution. I like puzzles that require a clever insight and clever execution, but are easy once you have the one bright idea." By contrast, he finds Rubik's cube a little bit frustrating, because even after you understand the basic principles you have to do a significant amount of memorization (see Box, **Speedcubing, Anyone?**, page 74).

However, Demaine says, "The most thrilling thing is to solve an open problem where you don't know what's true. For me, the best puzzle is a metapuzzle: Is this computationally tractable or intractable? Typically no one knows the answer to that."

> Rubik's cube [is] a little bit frustrating, because even after you understand the basic principles you have to do a significant amount of memorization.

"Street Sweeper". *In November 2009, at the peak of the worldwide epidemic of the H1N1 flu virus, a street sweeper in Tianjin, China sports a homemade facemask. Though their effectiveness was questionable, facemasks were a popular precautionary measure in many countries. (Photo courtesy of Jonah M. Kessel/ www.jonahkessel.com.)*

The Right Epidemic at the Right Time

IT DIDN'T TAKE LONG FOR Gerardo Chowell-Puente's life to be turned upside down. At the beginning of April, 2009, he was a mathematical epidemiologist investigating the transmission dynamics of influenza at Arizona State University and at the Fogarty International Center, a branch of the National Institutes of Health. But by month's end, he was consulting at the national health service in Mexico City, ground zero for the first influenza pandemic of the twenty-first century.

In February, in a town called La Gloria in Veracruz, Mexico, people had started falling sick with a mysterious respiratory illness, which killed two infants. By early April, as the disease spread to other cities, Mexican health authorities were alarmed enough to send samples to the U.S. and Canada to find out what they were dealing with. On April 23 the Public Health Agency of Canada identified it as a new version of a strain of flu called H1N1, which originated in pigs but also had snippets of bird flu and human flu DNA.

Gerardo Chowell-Puente. *(Photo courtesy of Gerardo Chowell-Puente.)*

By the time this news arrived, Chowell-Puente was already in Mexico City on behalf of Fogarty and was up to his ears in work. "The first question we had was whether this new virus was going to spread in a pandemic-like fashion," he says. "Our data was limited because Mexico didn't have a comprehensive virological surveillance system in place. The Ministry of Health requested medical institutions in all Mexican states to notify them of severe respiratory disease through an Internet-based platform. We started to do some calculations, which gave a reproduction number below 2 and above 1. That's an indication that it's going to spread. We also noted a disproportionate increase in hospitalizations and deaths among young adults, which resembles the patterns seen in old pandemics, like the one in 1918."

The early results showed that the virus might have a mortality rate of 0.6 percent, which would be comparable to the pandemics of 1957 and 1968 that had caused more than a million deaths worldwide. (This first mortality rate estimate would subsequently prove to be about thirty times too high.) All public events in Mexico City were canceled for a week. Surgical masks became the fashion statement of the day. Meanwhile, the World Health Organization raised its pandemic alert from phase 3 to phase 4 on April 27, from phase 4 to phase 5 (pandemic imminent) on April 29, and finally to the highest level, phase 6 (pandemic declared) on June 11. The world officially had its first flu pandemic in forty-one years.

Over the next few months, scientists like Chowell-Puente would continue to be in great demand, as policy makers and health services demanded answers about what might happen next. "It was on the one hand fun, but on the other hand extremely stressful," says Alessandro Vespignani, a physicist and epidemic modeler at Northeastern University. "It was not like regular scientific work. You are traveling to meetings and visiting crisis units, and people are calling you 24 hours a day."

Some of the questions that the modelers had to answer were: Can the influenza be contained at its source? (No.) How effective would a quarantine be? (Not very, although Hong Kong did quarantine the hotel at which its first case appeared.) How about school closures? (Mexico closed its schools nationwide, and about 400 schools in the U.S. followed suit.) How should we use our antiviral stockpiles—as a treatment for diagnosed cases or as prophylaxis for people who have been exposed but haven't gotten sick yet? When the drug companies finally get a vaccine ready, whom should we vaccinate—older people who are more at risk of dying, or younger people who cause most of the transmission?

None of these questions are easy. There is no time for experiments in the field, and history is an imperfect guide because every epidemic is different. Under the circumstances, a mathematical model is the only way to get objective and quantitative answers. The 2009 flu epidemic, as well as the SARS outbreak of 2003, were the first in which computer-based epidemic models were available to make predictions in real time.

In a strange coincidence, epidemiologists had already been on high alert for five years (see Figure 1). A different flu virus, called H5N1, had emerged in the early 2000s and caused more than 250 deaths worldwide by 2009. This avian flu could not be easily transmitted from human to human, and this kept its spread in check. However, the wrong set of mutations could make H5N1 contagious and touch off a pandemic, and many of the models were developed specifically with that possibility in mind.

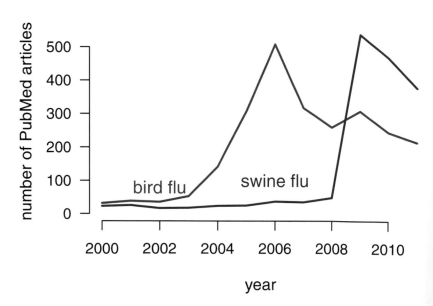

Figure 1. *Graph of the number of articles indexed in PubMed referring to "bird flu" and "swine flu" from 2000 to 2010. Epidemiologists were on high alert for a flu epidemic in the last half of the decade—but the one that materialized was not the one they expected. (Figure courtesy of Dennis Chao.)*

No one was expecting the swine flu to strike instead. But the mathematical models were ready and waiting. And the world got lucky in another way, too: The H1N1 flu was not as deadly as the early reports had suggested. "After June it was clear that it was not the end of the world," Vespignani says. The 2009 pandemic turned out to be the right pandemic at the right time, if such a thing is possible—a chance to iron out the logistics of responding to an old scourge in the modern computer age, but without the millions of fatalities that had taken place in 1918, 1957, and 1968.

The SIR Model and Beyond

The mathematical modeling of epidemics began long before the computer age. One of the first useful models was developed by Sir Ronald Ross, who received the Nobel Prize in 1902 in recognition of his work on malaria. However, malaria is a relatively complicated disease, which is transmitted by mosquitoes. The simplest starting point for human-to-human disease transmission (even today) is the SIR model, proposed by William Kermack and Anderson Gray McKendrick in 1927.

In the SIR model, a population of humans is divided into three compartments: the Susceptibles (S), Infected (I), and Recovered (R). The whole population has N people, and it is typically assumed that there are no deaths during the epidemic (although the model can be modified to include deaths from the disease or exogenous deaths if necessary).

In each unit of time, each person in the susceptible population is assumed to make a constant number (c) of contacts. Out of these contacts, a proportion equal to I/N will be with infected individuals. (This statement assumes that the population mixes in random fashion, which is one of the most debatable hypotheses behind the model.) Finally, because no disease is 100% contagious, some fraction r of these contacts will actually result in infection. When that happens, that person will leave the susceptible compartment and move into the infected compartment.

Thus the rate of decrease of the susceptible population ($-dS/dt$) equals the number of infectious contacts per unit time ($S \cdot c \cdot r \cdot I/N$). Usually the constant parameters $c \cdot r/N$ are lumped into a single number β, and the differential equation for the susceptible population is written:

$$\frac{dS}{dt} = -\beta SI.$$

Meanwhile the infected population increases as people catch the disease, and decreases as they recover. The per capita recovery rate is assumed to be constant and equal to α; or, to put it differently, the average person is infectious for a length of time equal to $1/\alpha$. Thus the infected population satisfies the following differential equation:

$$\frac{dI}{st} = \beta SI - \alpha I.$$

Similarly, it is possible to write a third differential equation for the number of recovered individuals R, but this is moot because after S and I are known, R can be computed directly from the equation $S + I + R = N$ (since the total population is assumed constant in this simplest version of the SIR model).

Thus the SIR model boils down to a system of two differential equations that are nonlinear, but only mildly so. Some of the nastier features of nonlinearity, such as chaos, do not occur in such a simple model, and it is very easy to analyze the course of the epidemic even without a computer. If the ratio $R_0 = \beta S_0 / \alpha$ is less than 1 (where S_0 is the initial number of susceptibles), then the epidemic never gets started: the number of infecteds eventually decreases to 0. However, if R_0 is greater than 1, the population of infecteds will initially grow exponentially:

$$I(t) \approx e^{(R_0 - 1)\alpha t}.$$

Eventually, as the "supply" of susceptibles dwindles, the epidemic will reach a peak and then $I(t)$ will start to decrease. The time and height of this peak can be predicted by solving the system of equations on a computer (see Figure 2). It is also possible to estimate the proportion of people who get infected, called the *attack rate* by epidemiologists.

This version of the SIR model is extremely simple, but just complicated enough to capture some key properties of epidemics and highlight some important parameters. First, it demonstrated the existence of a "tipping point," long before that phrase became the title of a bestselling book. The course of the epidemic depends entirely on whether the *reproduction number*, R_0, is greater than or less than 1. This number has a very concrete interpretation: It is the number of secondary infections caused by introducing one infectious individual into a fully susceptible population. As Chowell-Puente's comment above indicates, calculating R_0 is even today the first order of business for an epidemiologist. It even earned a mention in the 2011 Hollywood movie, *Contagion*.

The value of R_0 also gives epidemiologists a good idea how contagious an epidemic is, and how hard it will be to bring under control. One consequence of the SIR model is that you don't have to vaccinate everybody. In fact, if you vaccinate $(1 - 1/R_0)$ of the susceptible population, you will reduce the initial pool of susceptibles S_0 enough that the exponentially increasing phase does not occur and the epidemic will die out all by itself. For example, if $R_0 = 2$, you have to vaccinate half the population. If $R_0 = 1.4$, a typical estimate for the 2009 H1N1 pandemic, then you only need to vaccinate 2/7 (28 percent) of the population. The concept that even a partially vaccinated population can resist an epidemic is called "herd immunity."

Despite its broad applicability, the SIR model does suffer from some very obvious flaws. First, it is deterministic. If only life were so simple for epidemiologists! In reality, chance events can make a big difference. Also, the "constants" α and β, especially β, are not really constant. During an epidemic people can and do alter their behavior to reduce transmission. Governments may impose travel restrictions; schools may close; people may stay at home more (thus possibly *increasing* their exposure to family members, but decreasing their exposure to the outside).

Third, the assumption of random, homogeneous mixing of the population is obviously problematic. Different people vary greatly in their number of contacts. According to one study in Great Britain, school-aged children averaged about 33 conversational contacts per day in 2009, while senior citizens over age 65 averaged 4 a day. During school breaks, the number of contacts for children dropped to 16 a day. Such a big drop, within the group that transmits the disease most often, would strongly affect R_0. In addition, most contacts are far from random. They will be with family, classmates, co-workers, etc., while relatively few contacts will be truly unpredictable encounters, such as bumping into someone in the subway.

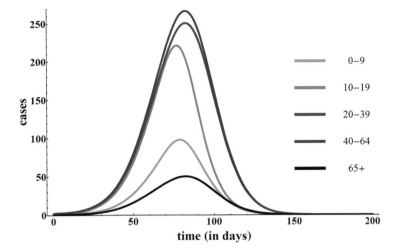

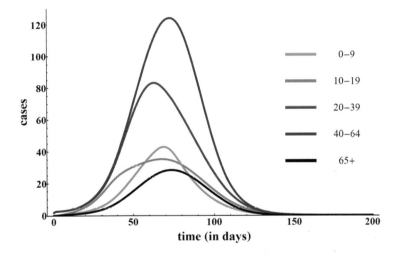

Figure 2. *Output of a deterministic SEIR (Susceptible-Exposed-Infected-Recovered) epidemic model, stratified by age. All age groups show an initial stage of exponential growth, followed by a peak and a rapid decrease as the pool of susceptibles becomes too small for the epidemic to sustain itself. This figure contrasts a "conventional" vaccination policy that targets high-risk groups first (top) and a policy that targets age groups with many contacts (especially ages 10–19) first (bottom). Mathematical models like SEIR make it possible to study detailed "what-if" scenarios. (Figures courtesy of Diana Hulman-Knipl, from D.H. Knipl and G. Röst, "Modeling the Strategies for Age-Specific Vaccination Scheduling During Influenza Pandemic Outbreaks,"* Mathematical Biosciences and Engineering, **8***(1), 2011, 123–139.)*

McKendrick and Kermack's model failed to capture another factor that could not even have been anticipated in 1927: the rise of international air travel. In past centuries, epidemics such as the Black Death traveled overland gradually, like a wave (see Figure 3a), taking years to infect a whole continent. But now, a disease can leap halfway across the world in a single day. In 2009 for example, the H1N1 virus reached Hong Kong by May 1, scarcely a week after the outbreak in Mexico became public knowledge.

Finally, not all diseases have the same natural history, and the SIR model has to be modified to describe them. Some diseases do not confer immunity. For such diseases, modelers can use the even simpler SIS model, in which a recovered person immediately becomes susceptible again. Other diseases may require the population to be divided into more compartments. For example, in influenza there are many asymptomatic cases, which are nevertheless contagious (at a lower level than the symptomatic ones). So the Infected compartment may need to be subdivided into Symptomatic and Asymptomatic. Vector-borne diseases, like malaria, may need several different equations to describe contacts between parasites and mosquitoes, mosquitoes and humans, etc. In a disease like Chagas' disease, which is conveyed by bedbugs, it may be better to think of the vectors infecting a household rather than the individuals in that household.

Advanced Models

For all the reasons above, mathematicians have continued to look for improvements to the basic SIR model, and sometimes developed completely different approaches. One idea was to incorporate a permanent network of contacts into the model,

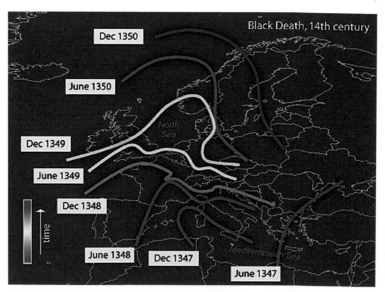

Figure 3a. *Disease transmission dynamics depend not only on the natural history of the pathogen, but also on the structure of human society. In the 1300s, the Black Death epidemic took three years to sweep across Europe. (Figure courtesy of the GLEAMviz Project (http://www.gleamviz.org).)*

instead of assuming random mixing over the whole population. This has several virtues: you can make the model population more heterogeneous, and bring in an explicit element of chance. For example, you can assume that when one person becomes infected, that person infects each of his or her contacts with a probability p.

Even though such a model is no longer deterministic, in many cases its average behavior can be analyzed rigorously, and it differs from the deterministic model in subtle ways. The naive SIR model tends to overestimate the severity of epidemics; uniform mixing of the population is in some sense a worst-case scenario. Network models still have a tipping point at $R_0 = 1$, but it becomes a softer tipping point. Below this value the disease still dies out. When $R_0 > 1$, the disease *can* set off an epidemic, but it is not inevitable. (The higher R_0 is, the higher the probability.) Also, the attack rate can no longer be predicted with certainty. The extent of the epidemic, if there is one, depends strongly on where in the network it started—in a highly connected cluster or in an area with few contacts.

Because of this sensitivity to the network structure, attention turned to more accurate descriptions of the kinds of contact networks that societies naturally form. Herbert Hethcote and James Yorke in the early 1980s showed that gonorrhea was primarily spread by a small group of "super spreaders" or highly connected people. On the theoretical side, in the 1990s, Duncan Watts and Steven Strogatz introduced the idea of small-world networks and Albert-László Barabasi studied scale-free networks. They and other researchers found that the threshold behavior of the epidemic could sometimes change drastically depending on their assumptions about the network.

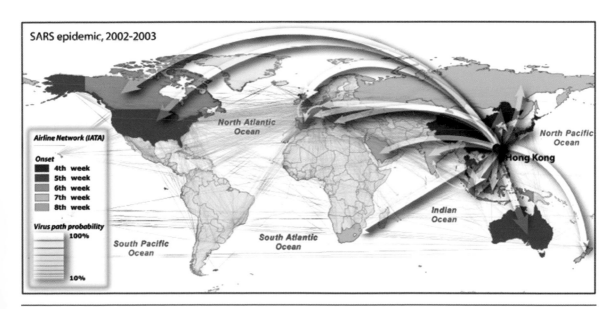

Figure 3b. *Disease transmission dynamics depend not only on the natural history of the pathogen, but also on the structure of human society. In 2003, the SARS epidemic leaped from continent to continent in weeks, thanks to air travel. For this reason, many epidemic models now explicitly incorporate a realistic version of the international air traffic network. (Figure courtesy of the GLEAMviz Project (http://www.gleamviz.org).)*

> ...[S]everal models independently confirmed that restricting international air travel would do almost nothing to stop a global pandemic. Even if the restrictions were 90 percent effective (a very optimistic assumption), they would at best slow the epidemic down by a week or two.

Another approach was to continue using a compartment model but refine the compartments. For example, each population could be separated into different age categories that reflect the different contact patterns and susceptibilities of younger and older people. In this case, the single reproduction number R_0 is replaced by a matrix K, called the next-generation matrix, in which the ij-th element represents the number of cases in age category j that result from the introduction of a single infectious individual in category i. The largest eigenvalue of K is R_0. However, just as in the network models, R_0 doesn't tell the whole story. Two next-generation matrices can have the same leading eigenvalue but give rise to epidemics with very different attack rates. In addition, the information in the next-generation matrix can be used to devise a vaccination strategy that treats different age groups in different ways—a consideration that became very important in 2009.

An interesting model that combines elements of network models and compartment models is called Global Epidemic and Mobility (GlEaM). Developed in the framework of a Europe-USA collaboration by Vespignani and his colleagues, GlEaM incorporates a weighted graph of 3362 airports, which account for 99 percent of worldwide air traffic. It splits the planet up geographically into a lattice of 15-by-15-arc-minute regions, each of which is assigned to the nearest airport. These regions define "metapopulations," within which the epidemic is modeled using a conventional compartment model with age stratification.

All of these models still use averages or statistical distributions to describe a large group of people. It might seem as if the ultimate model would simulate every single person as a unique individual. Thanks to increases in computing power, it has become possible to run such a model, called an "agent-based model," up to the scale of an entire country. Models like this have been developed at Los Alamos National Labs, Harvard University, and Imperial College London (see Figure 4). They have the advantage of being very understandable to policy makers. In a compartment model, you can talk about trying to reduce the infectivity by 30 percent, but what does this mean? How do you actually do it? By contrast, in an agent-based model, you can literally close the schools, close the workplaces, or close the airports, and see what effect that has.

"These models are very satisfying to epidemiologists, but they're not a panacea," says Carlos Castillo-Chavez, a mathematician at Arizona State. Agent-based models are very computationally intensive. They also make many more assumptions than compartment models do—some of which can never be validated. And they are certainly less transparent than compartment models, whose basic behavior can often be proved theoretically.

Already before the 2009 epidemic, the troika of network models, compartment models, and agent-based models was beginning to change epidemiologists' minds on certain issues. For example, around 2006, several models independently confirmed that restricting international air travel would do almost nothing to stop a global pandemic. Even if the restrictions were 90 percent effective (a very optimistic assumption), they would at best slow the epidemic down by a week or two.

"When these studies first came out, I was at a meeting where a lot of ministers of health said that they were going to do it anyway," says Marc Lipsitch of Harvard University, a co-author of one of the studies on travel restrictions. "But by 2009, people had internalized these results and realized that border closures didn't make much sense. A few places did try to close their borders—Hong Kong was one—but they had very specific reasons. They knew it wasn't going to work in the long run, but thought that buying a week or two would do some good. It wasn't done blindly."

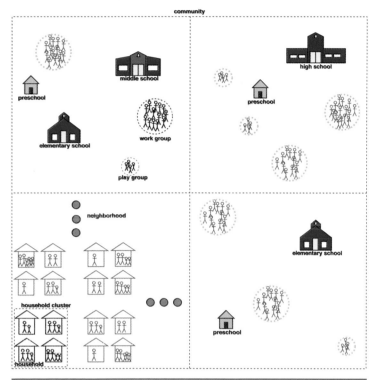

Figure 4. *Conceptual illustration of the FluTE agent-based model. Individuals are grouped into households, households into clusters, clusters into neighborhoods, and neighborhoods into communities. At each level the chance of transmission from one individual to another will depend on whether they both belong to a common group, such as a work group, play group, or school. (Figure courtesy of Dennis Chao, from Chao, D.L. et al., FluTE, a Publicly Available Stochastic Infuenza Epidemic Simulation Model. PLoS Biol. 6 (1): e1000656, (2010).)*

Lessons Learned from 2009

While mathematical models had proven their worth before, for example in the study of diseases like gonorrhea and HIV, as well as past influenza epidemics like the 1918-9 Spanish flu, 2009 was the first chance to apply them to an emerging flu epidemic in real time.

A first issue was the inaccurate data that came out in the early stages of the epidemic, particularly in Mexico. With no existing surveillance system, the initial estimates of the number of cases had to be based on reports from hospitals and physicians. This meant that only the more severe cases were reported

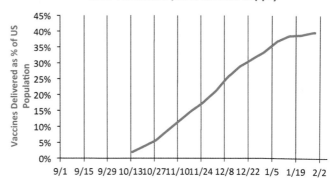

2009 Pandemic H1N1 vaccine supply

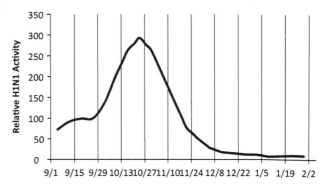

2009 Pandemic H1N1 activity

Figure 5. *In 2009, vaccines did not become available in the U.S. until the epidemic was nearly at its peak. The blue curve represents delivery of the vaccine; the effectiveness date is estimated to be 3 weeks later. (Figure courtesy of Richard Lipsitch.)*

at first, and the number of less-severe cases was vastly under-counted. The magnitude of the undercount started to become apparent when data began coming in from other countries.

"There were fewer cases, more readily ascertained, in countries where people returned as travelers from Mexico," says Lipsitch. "You can count the number of person-days of traveler experience in Mexico and then compare it to Mexicans. This is not an exact science; there's a huge assumption because where travelers go is not necessarily where Mexicans go. Nevertheless, we could extrapolate that there must be between 10,000 and 100,000 cases [in Mexico], at a time when there were maybe 1000 being reported."

This kind of bias, called ascertainment bias, leads to an over-estimate of the severity of the epidemic. But the opposite kind of bias is also possible. In the SARS epidemic of 2003, the fatality rate was *underestimated* at first because of "censorship bias." Early in the epidemic, cases that would ultimately be fatal were reported as non-fatal because the patients hadn't died yet. This bias makes the disease seem less severe than it is. "In the spring of 2009, it was difficult to estimate the more severe bias," Lipsitch says. Only in late summer did it become appar-

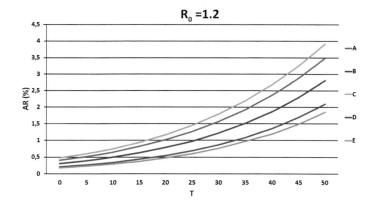

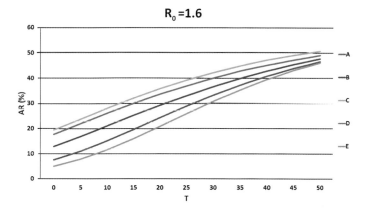

Figure 6. *In a simulated flu epidemic, a one-month delay in availability of a vaccine causes the attack rate (number of people infected) to more than double. Horizontal axis, T, shows the delay in days between the start of the epidemic and the start of vaccination. (Colors correspond to different immunization strategies; A = Conventional, E = Optimal based on age-specific contact numbers; AR = attack rank, R_0 = reproduction number.) (Figure courtesy of Diana Hulman-Knipl, op. cit.)*

ent that the ascertainment bias was much more important than the censorship bias, and the fatality rate for the H1N1 virus was closer to 0.02 percent than 0.6 percent.

Ironically, the scarcity of fatal cases (though welcome news for victims of the disease) created other difficulties. "This was a real challenge that we didn't appreciate in advance," says Lipsitch. "Because we had focused on a severe epidemic, no one had asked whether we should scale back on interventions in a milder pandemic. There were a lot of decisions to be made, questions of scale and timing of interventions, that you just wouldn't ask if people were dying in large numbers."

One potentially effective intervention that turned into something of a fiasco in 2009 was vaccination (see Figures 5 and 6). If the world were depending on vaccines to head off the next flu pandemic, H1N1 proved that we have a long way to go, because the first vaccines did not become available until October—six months after the epidemic began, and shortly before the epidemic reached its fall peak. Even then they were not available everywhere, or in sufficient quantities.

Until 2008, the CDC had recommended that children under 2 years and adults over 50 years of age should be vaccinated for seasonal flu. In 2008, children from ages 5 to 18 were added to the recommended category.

If vaccines are going to be late or scarce or only partially effective, computer models become even more important in determining how to use them to have the greatest impact. A provocative study by Jan Medlock of Oregon State and Alison Galvani of Yale concluded, "previous and new recommendations from the U.S. Centers for Disease Control... both for the novel swine-origin influenza and, particularly, for seasonal influenza, are suboptimal for all measures." Until 2008, the CDC had recommended that children under 2 years and adults over 50 years of age should be vaccinated for seasonal flu. In 2008, children from ages 5 to 18 were added to the recommended category. Using a compartment model, Medlock and Galvani simulated a wide variety of scenarios in which there are insufficient doses to prevent an epidemic (20 million, 40 million, or 60 million doses); different mortality patterns (the 1918 and 1957 epidemics were used as models); and different objectives (minimizing deaths, years of life lost, total illness, or cost to society—all laudable objectives, but only one can be achieved at a time). In only one case—with the smallest number of doses available, the most lethal illness, and the goal of minimizing deaths—does it ever make sense to vaccinate people over 50. And in almost every case, the 5 to 18 age group is the most important. "A simple way to think about it is that vaccinating schoolkids keeps their grandparents from getting infected and dying, being hospitalized, et cetera," Medlock says. Other epidemiologists disagree with their conclusions for the swine flu epidemic, noting that vaccines became available even later than in their simulations.

Ira Longini's group at the Fred Hutchinson Cancer Research Center in Seattle used an agent-based model, called FluTE, to study the effect that the vaccine would have had if it had been available a month earlier, or not at all. Across the U.S., the attack rate of the flu was 18.5 percent. With no vaccine at all, they estimated that the attack rate would have been 21.5 percent. If the vaccine had become available one month earlier, it would have been cut all the way to 13.5 percent. According to the model, the vaccine saved 1900 lives and 44,000 hospitalizations in the U.S.; but if it had come a month earlier, it would have saved 4600 lives and 109,000 hospitalizations. Even in a relatively mild epidemic, this shows how precious every day is.

The mathematical models provided some very good advice, most of it of the "don't-panic" variety. FluTE and GLEaM both predicted the early (late-October) peak of the fall wave, and indicated that there would be no third wave. Longini's group advised the Los Angeles Public Health Department not to close schools and not to use antiviral medicines to treat the early cases (which can lead to the development of drug resistance).

Still, there were some important lessons learned for future pandemics. One has to do with the use of the word "pandemic" itself. "Not all pandemics are created equal," Castillo-Chavez says. "There needs to be some sort of estimate of pandemic severity, because the decisions that people take have tremendous economic consequences." The World Health Organization has a rating system for the *likelihood* of a pandemic, but no corresponding system for its *severity*—it has nothing, for example, like the Category 1-5 rating system for hurricanes.

In some countries, says Castillo-Chavez, policy decisions still need to be more science-based. "We need to depoliticize the process," he says. "In Mexico there was almost a competition between the political parties to see which party could be perceived as doing the most for the population. I think that eventually this might have gotten in the way of admitting faster that this was not a severe pandemic."

And virtually everywhere, the modelers agree, the data-collection process needs to be better integrated with the modeling process. Modelers need real-world data as fast as possible to constrain parameters like α and β in the SIR model, let alone the many more parameters in more complicated models. Otherwise, their models are little better than an educated guess.

"There is not enough existing infrastructure to interface the models with surveillance data," says Joseph Wu of the University of Hong Kong. "In 2009 we were still at an early phase of integration. Even now, we are still making our best effort to tell people that do surveillance, 'This is what we need.'" A particular bone of contention is serological surveillance—taking massive numbers of blood samples in order to get ground truth on how many people have antibodies to the virus. This information would help pin down the most uncertain information early in an epidemic: how many susceptibles there are and how many mild cases there are. But it would be a major public health undertaking, which might draw skilled personnel away from other important tasks like developing a vaccine.

According to Lipsitch, the 2009 pandemic also demonstrated the need to think about how to make decisions with less data. It's fine to come up with an immunization strategy based on a complicated model that predicts attack rates, deaths, and the timing of the epidemic's peak. But in the early days of an epidemic, you may not have enough information yet to estimate those things. Lipsitch and Chowell-Puente have both written papers on devising a vaccination strategy that would use only early-days data. According to Chowell-Puente, a simple "adaptive vaccination" strategy, in which the number of doses allocated to each age group is proportional to the cases that have already occurred in that group during the first few weeks of the pandemic, performed better at reducing hospitalizations and deaths than the CDC's recommended policy at the time.

As the latest health scare recedes into the past, all of the modelers are very aware that their work is far from done. There are any number of other diseases, some of them more complicated than influenza: dengue, Chagas' disease, sexually transmitted diseases, endemic diseases, and the list goes on. Epidemiologists and mathematical modelers are working on all of them.

However, the opening of lines of communication between modelers, public-health workers, and policy makers is one of the most positive outcomes of the 2009 pandemic. "There are now multiple people with the CDC, WHO, and many health departments around this country and elsewhere who know and can talk to multiple modelers," says Lipsitch. "That link has been built in a way that was beginning before the pandemic but has really accelerated as a result of it."

> It's fine to come up with an immunization strategy based on a complicated model that predicts attack rates, deaths, and the timing of the epidemic's peak. But in the early days of an epidemic, you may not have enough information yet to estimate those things.

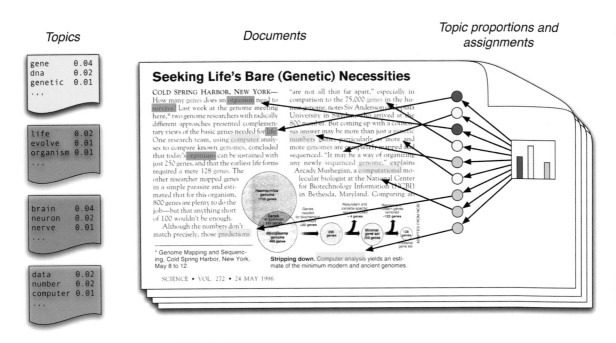

Figure 1. *A "generative model" of documents used in topic modeling. At left are the available topics. Note that a "topic" is just a list of words with corresponding frequencies. To generate a document, the author first chooses a probability distribution on the available topics (far right). Next, to compose any given word, he draws a topic at random from that probability distribution (middle right). For example, he decides that the third word of the document will be chosen from the yellow topic. Finally, he draws a word at random from that topic's word list ("genes"). (Figure courtesy of David M. Blei, from David M. Blei, "Probabilistic Topic Models," Communications of the ACM, April 2012, pp. 77–84.)*

Thinking Topically

OVER THE LAST TEN YEARS, CYBER-BULLYING has turned into one of the perils of adolescence in the Internet age. Highly publicized suicides like those of Megan Meier in 2006 and Tyler Clementi in 2010—and many others—have focused attention on the issue all the way up to the White House.

While adults might like to stop cyber-bullying or to recognize the warning signs of suicide, there are some obstacles. The volume of messages sent on social websites is huge, and it is not always easy to penetrate the teen-aged mind. Consider this text message:

"My bf doesn't luv me anymore. im kinda sucks, kinda scared want me life 2 end."

Thousands of anonymous messages like this one have been posted on a website for teenagers called A Thin Line (http://www.athinline.org). Is it a threat to commit suicide? Is it a case of harmless teenage "drama"?

Karthik Dinakar, a graduate student in natural language processing at MIT, has written a computer program that attempts to do what grownups can't: to classify text messages according to their content and search for other messages like them. (For example, in the above message the two main topics—identified by the machine but named by Dinakar—are "breakup heartache" and "feeling scared.")

Upon finding a close enough match in A Thin Line's database, Dinakar's program displays the related story to the person who has just posted his or her own story. "For suicidal teenagers, the very fact that we show them there are other people going through the same things is really important," says Dinakar. "Teenagers think the world begins and ends with them, and we want to break this pattern with what we call reflective thinking."

Dinakar's work has already gotten him invited to a 2011 White House symposium on cyber-bullying. He donated his code to the MTV television network, which sponsors A Thin Line. MTV was impressed enough to make it a regular feature on its website. While the program is intended to benefit the teenagers directly, Dinakar says that it will also help researchers gather data on the extent of abuse and harassment in teenage social networks. "For the very first time we will be analyzing cyber-bullying on a very big scale," Dinakar says. "It will be useful for psychologists and for lawmakers to see what teenagers are doing."

The same statistical methods used to identify the varieties of teenage angst can be used for a variety of other purposes. Dinakar's program uses a tool called latent Dirichlet allocation (LDA), invented in 2003, which is being used more and more frequently to comb through large databases of documents. The idea is to go beyond keywords to identify what documents are actually about, and to see how the topics in a large database

Karthik Dinakar *(Photo courtesy of Karthik Dinakar.)*

evolve over time. "As of 2012, I think that topic modeling is one of the hottest things in digital humanities," says Matthew Jockers, a professor of English at the University of Nebraska. "For example, my training is in Irish studies and Irish-American literature. We've often written about the way that Irish people sympathized with the plight of slaves in America in the 1800s. Previously, we would have been sitting in my office trading books, saying, 'Here's an Irish book addressing slavery, isn't that interesting.' Now I can tell you which 250 books deal with slavery."

From Dirichlet to Rock-and-Roll

The most popular topic model, latent Dirichlet allocation, is itself a pretty hot scientific topic. The term was coined by David Blei, Andrew Ng, and Michael I. Jordan in 2003. In less than ten years, their paper (also called "Latent Dirichlet Allocation") has become one of the 100 most-cited articles in the history of computer science. "We were in the right place at the right time," says Blei, who is now at Princeton University. "Suddenly, after 2003, there were all these big document data sets and people wanted to do unsupervised learning on them." An example is the Stanford Literary Lab, a database that Jockers co-developed with Franco Moretti, which contains 3400 digitized English-language novels from the nineteenth century, or roughly half the novels from that period that are still in existence. Other well-known book digitization projects include Project Gutenberg, the Library of Congress's "American Memory," and of course Google Books.

Latent Dirichlet allocation starts out with what one might generously call a computer's view or perhaps a Martian's view of how humans write a document. It bears little resemblance to how we really write, but a healthy suspension of disbelief is the first requirement.

In the world of LDA, every document belongs to a corpus, such as "nineteenth-century fiction" or "scientific research articles" or "posts to A Thin Line." Within that corpus, authors are free to choose from a certain set of topics or, occasionally, invent their own. The writers of articles for *Science* magazine, for example, write very often about genomics. They write somewhat less often about mathematics, and very rarely about rock-and-roll music.

Each topic implies a particular word distribution. If the topic of an article is genomics, for instance, we would expect to see a high frequency of words like "gene" or "DNA," and not many words like "Beatles" or "guitar." An important point is that a *topic*, as understood in LDA, is nothing more than a bag of words with associated probabilities (e.g., "gene"—0.04 percent, "DNA"—0.02 percent). The algorithm does not interpret the semantic content of this bag of words. In this sense, it belongs more to the discipline of statistics than to artificial intelligence. It is up to human scholars (if they want) to look in the bag, to see words like "Beatles," "guitar," etc., and interpret the topic as being "rock-and-roll."

A second key point about the LDA model is that *documents usually have more than one topic.* Even an article that is mostly about genomics will still touch on a number of other topics. The author may, for instance, write a document in which 40 percent of the words come from the genomics category, 30 percent from evolutionary biology, 20 percent from data analysis, and 10 percent from the study of a specific disease, say diabetes (see Figure 1, page 98). This insight seems obvious in retrospect but was not previously obvious to specialists on text mining.

More formally, the LDA model assumes that a document consists of words 1 to N, chosen from a vocabulary V. Thus the document can be written as a vector in V^N : $\mathbf{w} = (w_1, \ldots, w_N)$. A topic z is a probability measure on the space of words; we can call the space of all such measures $P(V)$. The corpus contains a certain set of topics, $T = \{z_1, \ldots, z_M\} \subset P(V)$. Before even writing a single word, the author of a document decides what it will be about. In the view of LDA, this means that he selects a probability distribution $\theta = (\theta_1, \ldots, \theta_M)$ on T. Each θ_i represents the probability that any given word of the document will be about topic z_i. To write word w_j, the author first rolls a die that is weighted according to the probabilities θ. The die tells him which topic to select a word from. To select a word from that topic, he rolls another die, which is weighted according to the probability distribution z_j. After N rounds of this procedure, the author has chosen the word vector $\mathbf{w}$ as well as a topic vector $\mathbf{z} = (z_1, \ldots, z_N) \in T^N$.

So far no mention has been made of the Dirichlet distribution. In fact, you could use any probability distribution you like for θ, and get your own customized topic model. However, the most popular choice is the Dirichlet distribution, which is flexible enough to fit lots of different corpuses but at the same time not so flexible that it overfits the data. Specifically, the probability density for a mixture of topics θ is:

$$p(\theta|\alpha) = c(\alpha)\theta_1^{\alpha_1 - 1} \ldots \theta_M^{\alpha_M - 1}.$$

The constant $c(\alpha)$ is not important—its only role is to make the total probability equal to 1—but the vector of nonnegative weights, called "hyperparameters," $\alpha = (\alpha_1, \ldots, \alpha_M)$, does matter. The hyperparameters describe the shape of the Dirichlet distribution. For instance, if $\alpha = (1, 1, \ldots, 1)$, then the corpus has a flat probability distribution, in which every mixture of topics is equally likely. The higher the weight α_i, the more the probability is skewed toward $\theta_i = 1$ (meaning that documents are more likely to be about topic i) (see Figure 2, next page). This is one way that LDA takes into account that "rock-and-roll" is less likely in the *Science* corpus than "genomics".

LDA also includes a second hyperparameter β that modifies the selection of words. This parameter shows how authors are allowed some flexibility to reach outside the bag, coin new words, etc. Putting it all together, the LDA model postulates a joint probability distribution on topics, topic vectors, and word vectors that takes the following form:

$$p(\theta, z, w|\alpha, \beta) = p(\theta|\alpha) \prod_{i=1}^{N} p(z_i|\theta)p(w_i|z_i, \beta).$$

The first probability distribution on the right-hand side is a Dirichlet distribution and the other two (after the product symbol) are multinomial.

Blei, Ng, and Jordan did not, of course, invent LDA from

> [Y]ou could use any probability distribution you like for θ, and get your own customized topic model. However, the most popular choice is the Dirichlet distribution, which is flexible enough to fit lots of different corpuses but at the same time not so flexible that it overfits the data.

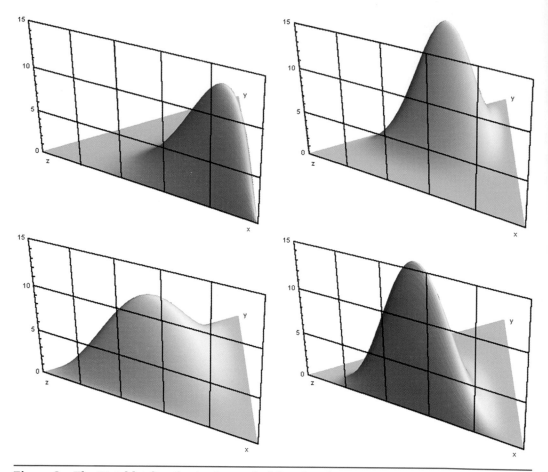

Figure 2. *The Dirichlet distribution is a probability distribution on the simplex $\theta_1 + \theta_2 + ldots + \theta_n = 1$. In this figure, $n = 3$. The shape of the distribution (e.g., the location, height, and "sharpness" of the peak) is controlled by "hyperparameters" $\alpha_1, \alpha_2, \alpha_3$. Clockwise from upper left, the hyperparameters here are $(6, 2, 2)$, $(3, 7, 5)$, $(6, 2, 6)$, and $(2, 3, 4)$. In the context of latent Dirichlet allocation, beliefs about the topic distribution of a document can be updated simply by changing the hyperparameters. (Figure downloaded from Wikipedia (Public Domain.))*

scratch. It grew out of earlier, simpler models in the machine learning and speech recognition communities.

In the simplest model, a "unigram" model, every document is about the same topic. A slightly more complicated version is the "mixture of unigrams" model, where every document is about one topic but the topic is chosen from a probability distribution. Finally, the immediate antecedent of LDA was Thomas Hofmann's probabilistic latent semantic indexing (pLSI) method (1999). Hofmann had the crucial insight of allowing multiple topics, but his model had one drawback: it is not *generative*—that is, it does not explain how new documents come into existence.

Figure 3 illustrates the difference between LDA and pLSI. In pLSI, the probability distribution for θ (the topic mixture for a new document) is completely empirical. It is concentrated on the dots in the figure, which correspond to the previous documents in the corpus. By contrast, the Dirichlet distribution in LDA is smooth, like a gentle hill whose contour lines are illustrated in the figure. This actually makes LDA *simpler* than pLSI. It depends on M parameters (typically tens to hundreds), while

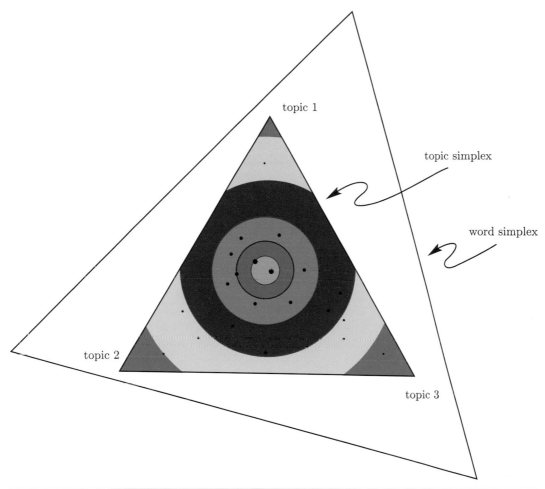

topic 1

topic simplex

word simplex

topic 2

topic 3

Figure 3. *Topic models in a language consisting of three words. The topics are points in the triangle in three-space defined by the equation $\theta_1 + \theta_2 + \theta_3 = 1$ and the inequalities $\theta_i \geq 0$ for all i. This is the "word simplex." In pLSI, the probability distribution for topics is empirical, and consists of a separate point for each document in the corpus. In LDA, the probability distribution is a Dirichlet distribution, whose contours are shown in the figure. (Adapted from a figure provided by David M. Blei.)*

the number of parameters in pLSI is the number of documents in the corpus (typically thousands).

"It was a technicality, but in retrospect an important one," Blei says. "The practical answer to why LDA has enabled all these applications is that you can embed a generative model into more complicated models. This is hard to do if the parameters index the documents themselves."

Reversing the Process: Inference

The LDA model produces a joint probability distribution, $p(\theta, \mathbf{z}, \mathbf{w} | \alpha, \beta)$, on all topic vectors and word vectors, conditioned on the choice of the Dirichlet parameters α and β. Once $\mathbf{z}$ and β are known it is easy to compute the probability of a specific word vector, or $p(\mathbf{w} | \mathbf{z}, \beta)$.

But in a real-life case, the statistician faces exactly the opposite situation. The word vectors $\mathbf{w}$ of the documents are known; the challenge is to estimate the hidden variables (θ and $\mathbf{z}$) and the hyperparameters (α and β). To infer the topics in a given document ("*My bf doesn't luv me...*") we want to know the likelihood of topic vector **z** given word vector **w**. In symbols, we want to compute $p(\mathbf{z}|\mathbf{w}, \beta)$.

This kind of "inverse probability" problem is made to order for Bayesian statistics. By Bayes' theorem,

$$p(\mathbf{z}|\mathbf{w}, \beta) = \frac{p(\mathbf{w}|\mathbf{z}, \beta)p(\mathbf{z}|\beta)}{p(\mathbf{w}|\beta)}.$$

The terms in the numerator are easy to compute; they come straight from the LDA model. But to compute the denominator, you would have to sum the probabilities $p(\mathbf{w}|\mathbf{z}, \beta)$ over every possible topic vector **z**. The number of possible topic vectors is M^N. No computer today or in the foreseeable future will be able to compute a sum that might run to $100^{10,000}$ terms.

Fortunately, in recent years, approximate methods have been developed that allow *estimation* of these probabilities in a reasonable time on a fast computer. (One of these methods is called Markov chain Monte Carlo, or MCMC. See "Instant Randomness," *What's Happening in the Mathematical Sciences*, vol. 8.) Technically speaking, the choice of an inference method is separate from LDA itself. You can use LDA with MCMC, or you can use LDA with other methods, such as a variational method that was described in the original paper of Blei, Ng and Jordan. For online, real-time updating, Blei considers the variational method superior. For a smaller corpus, many people prefer MCMC because it is easier to grasp intuitively.

In the context of LDA, Markov chain Monte Carlo works as follows (see Figure 4). You start by assuming a completely random distribution of words among topics and a flat prior distribution for the parameters. Then you go through your corpus one document at a time, estimating the most likely topic-to-word assignment for that document and then updating the word-to-topic probability distribution accordingly. This update simply involves counting the number of occurrences of each word with each topic and performing a weighted average with the previous probabilities. If, for example, you see that the word "gene" has been assigned more often to topic 5, you will increase the probability of "gene" being assigned to that topic

A generalized[3] fundamental[146] theorem[267] of **natural**[280] **selection**[280] is derived[233] for **populations**[280] incorporating[149] both **genetic**[280] and **cultural**[280] transmission[25]. The phenotype[3] is determined[17] by an arbitrary[3] number[257] of **multiallelic**[3] loci[3] with two[271]-factor[60] **epistasis**[280] and an arbitrary[149] linkage[3] map[3], as well as by **cultural**[280] transmission[25] from the **parents**[280]. **Generations**[280] are discrete[69] but partially[275] overlapping[146], and **mating**[280] may be **nonrandom**[280] at either the **genotypic**[280] or the **phenotypic**[280] level[199] (or both). I show[25] that **cultural**[280] transmission[25] has several[173] important[173] implications[17] for the **evolution**[280] of **population**[280] **fitness**[280], most notably[230] that there is a time[72] lag[72] in the response[213] to **selection**[280] such that the future[287] **evolution**[280] depends[105] on the past **selection**[280] history[280] of the **population**[280].

Figure 4. *Inferring topics from words in a document. Topic modelers use an iterative Monte Carlo method to decide which topics are present and in what frequency, and which words refer to that topic. In this document, topic 250 is present at high frequency, and is represented by words such as "natural," "selection," and "genetic." (© 2004 National Academy of Sciences. From "Finding Scientific Topics," by Thomas Griffiths and Mark Steyvers,* Proceedings of the National Academy of Sciences, *Volume* **101**, *Supp. 1, pp. 5228–5235, April 6, 2004.)*

in the future. One of the technical advantages of the Dirichlet distribution is that you can do this by simply changing the parameter β.

Next, staying with the same document, you assume that the revised β is correct and you change the topic-to-word assignments. Now that topic 5 has become more likely, you might notice that it also includes the word "DNA". When you see the word "DNA" in your document, you are now more likely to think that it came from topic 5 rather than topic 72, and so you will change its topic assignment. This is the way that inference in the LDA model captures word associations. After recomputing all the topic assignments in your document, now you proceed to the topic probabilities for the entire corpus, which were given by the distribution θ. In light of the evidence in your new document, you might want to increase the corpus-wide probability that documents will contain topic 5. The updated topic distribution θ will again be Dirichlet, only with a slightly revised parameter α.

Finally, now that you have updated your corpus-wide parameters and your document-specific topic vector $\mathbf{z}$, you are ready to proceed to the next document. At first, each new document will significantly affect the topic distribution and the word-to-topic distribution, but after a few hundred or a few thousand iterations, these probability distributions will usually stabilize. (This is one reason to use large corpuses of documents.)

What Hath Dirichlet Wrought?

One reason that LDA has been so popular is that it works amazingly well. The topics that it generates simply make sense, and it is sometimes hard to believe that they were the output of a program that has no idea what the words mean. As Scott Weingart, a graduate student in information science at Indiana University, writes: "When a newcomer sees the results of LDA for the first time, they are immediately taken by how intuitive they seem."

Figure 5a (next page) shows two of the 500 leading topics from Jockers' database of 19th-century novels. The topics are portrayed as word clouds, with larger words being more frequently used in that topic. As mentioned before, the LDA algorithm does not interpret these word clouds. But a human can. Jockers describes the first topic as "American slavery," and the second one as "afternoon tea."

LDA has made possible a new approach to humanities that could never be conceived of before: a large-scale approach that tracks trends in a corpus over time, over different geographical regions, or across different communities. For example, it gives quantitative substance to the anecdotal evidence that Irish writers were interested in slavery. As shown in Figure 5b (next page), the number of appearances of this topic in Irish literature shot up in the 1860s. "A lot of that is attributable to one author, Thomas Mayne Reid, who traveled extensively in America," Jockers said. "But even if we compensate for the Mayne Reid effect, the Irish are twice as interested in depicting this as the British." For another example, you can see the gradual increase in popularity of the "afternoon tea" topic throughout the nineteenth century, especially in Britain—evidence of the British love affair with tea and all of its associated rituals.

> LDA has made possible a new approach to humanities that could never be conceived of before: a large-scale approach that tracks trends in a corpus over time, over different geographical regions, or across different communities.

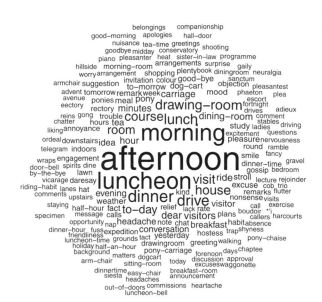

Figure 5a. *Word clouds representing two topics ("American Slavery" and "Afternoon Tea") that are common in 19th century literature. Sizes of the words are proportional to their frequency in the topic. The topics and words in them are identified by computer; the names of the topics are supplied after the fact by a human expert. (Figure © Matthew Jockers, 2012.)*

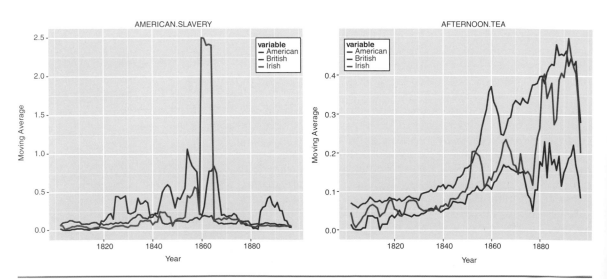

Figure 5b. *Frequency of the topics "American Slavery" and "Afternoon Tea" as a function of time in American, British, and Irish literature. LDA makes it possible to identify trends over an entire corpus of documents that would be far too voluminous for any human expert to read. (Figure © Matthew Jockers, 2012.)*

In some cases it is actually possible to compare the topics identified by LDA with human-identified topics. In 2004, Thomas Griffiths of Stanford and Mark Steyvers of MIT analyzed all 28,154 abstracts published in the *Proceedings of the National Academy of Sciences* between 1991 and 2001. Their study identified 300 of the most common topics. This corpus happens to offer a gold standard to compare them to, because authors of *PNAS* papers are expected to assign their paper to one of 33 categories such as Psychology or Immunology.

For each category, Griffiths and Steyvers identified the topic that is most specific to that category. For Psychology, the most characteristic topic has a word cloud dominated by the words "cortex brain subjects task areas." For Immunology, the leading topic was "cells cell antigen lymphocytes CD4." As in the case of Jocker's project, these word clouds make intuitive sense.

Having identified reasonable categories, Griffiths and Steyvers went on to discover some interesting patterns. The categories Ecology, Geology, and Geophysics all had the same leading topic, which begins "species global climate CO2 water." This could be called the climate change subtopic, and a historian of science might use this as evidence of the emergence of a new science spanning all three of these more classic disciplines. Not surprisingly, this was one of the three "hottest topics" in the database, with the most rapid increase in popularity between 1991 and 2001. The other two hottest topics in the *PNAS* corpus were gene knockout techniques ("mice deficient normal gene...") and programmed cell death ("apoptosis death cell induced...") (see Figure 6). Griffiths and Steyvers noted that the latter topic was the subject of the 2002 Nobel Prize in Physiology. Could LDA be used to forecast Nobel Prizes in the future?

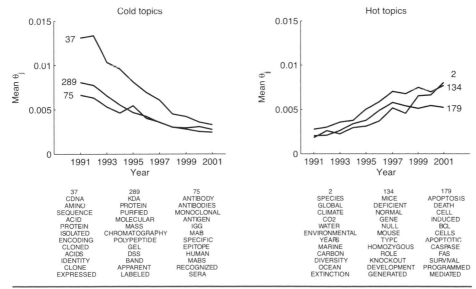

Figure 6. *Trends in topics observed in PNAS articles, as inferred by latent Dirichlet allocation. "Cold topics" decreased in frequency over the decade 1991-2001, while "hot topics" increased. (Figure © 2004 National Academy of Sciences. From "Finding Scientific Topics," by Thomas Griffiths and Mark Steyvers,* Proceedings of the National Academy of Sciences, *Volume* **101**, *Supp. 1, pp. 5228–5235, April 6, 2004.)*

These examples show that latent Dirichlet allocation does much more than provide lists of words: it also provides a new way of exploring digital data and generating hypotheses. Other applications of topic modeling have expanded the definitions of "topic" and "document," which Blei points out are only terms of convenience to make the statistical model more understandable.

In population biology, for instance, the "documents" are genomes, the "words" are alleles (distinct sequences of DNA), and the "topics" are ancestral populations. A person may have ancestors in more than one group—a key feature of what Matthew Stephens and Jonathan Pritchard of the University of Chicago named the "admixture model." Using their admixture model, which is mathematically equivalent to LDA[1] and discovered independently of it, Stephens and Pritchard identified five ancestral populations of *Helicobacter pylori*, a microbe found in the human gut, which originated in different parts of the world. They used this information to reconstruct the likely patterns of human migration, such as the entry of two distinct populations of Neolithic farmers (from the Urals and the Near East) into Europe.

David Mimno, a computer scientist at Princeton University, analyzed a database of 6000 artifacts found in Pompeii, which had been coded by room type (574 rooms of 22 different types) and artifact type (240 different types) by archaeologist Penelope Allison. In this case the "documents" are rooms, the "words" are artifact types, and the "topics" are functional groups (such as items used in food preparation). A room has a probability distribution over activities that will go on in the room, and the activities have a distribution over objects.

While his study broke no new ground (figuratively speaking), Mimno did confirm two of Allison's conjectures: that an object known as a *casseruola* ("casserole dish") was not actually used in food preparation, and that a room known as a *cubiculum* ("bedroom") was not actually used for sleeping. In other words, the items had been misnamed by archaeologists.

These examples inevitably raise questions about the reproducibility and accuracy of topic inference. Because the inference procedure uses a random process, the topics identified are not entirely consistent from one run to the next. They always include some "junk topics," consisting (for example) of abbreviations and misspelled words or (for another example) words that are primarily found in documents by one author. Even the valid topics will contain some spurious words. In practice, LDA needs a human subject matter expert to sort out the wheat from the chaff, although Blei and Mimno have done some work on automatic identification of junk topics. The problem of finding a credibility interval or a significance test is still wide open.

There is some tendency among users of LDA, especially in the humanities, to treat it as a cookbook procedure, when in fact it can be extended and modified in many ways depending on the nature of the data. Blei has developed versions that relax

---

[1]One minor difference between the biological application and the humanities is that the number of ancestral populations is likely to be small (five in the example below), while the number of topics in a literary corpus is usually tens to hundreds.

the "bag of words" assumption, allowing some correlation between nearby words; versions where the topics can change over time; versions that do not prescribe the number of topics ahead of time; and versions that incorporate metadata to improve the topic discovery. "I always try to impart to my collaborators that I don't want to know what methods you know, I want to know about your data," Blei says.

Back to Cyber-Bullying

When Karthik Dinakar started his graduate studies at MIT in 2010, he could scarcely have expected to be invited to the White House less than a year later. That fall, he says, he had to come up with a research topic for one of his classes. "I was just watching Anderson Cooper: 360 on CNN, and he did a special segment on cyber-bullying," Dinakar says. "This was just after a kid in New Jersey had thrown himself off a bridge after someone posted something nasty about him. I thought, what about using machine learning techniques to detect some of these nasty things?"

Dinakar's first project used data provided by Formspring, a social networking company, and he presented the results at the International Conference on Weblogs and Social Media (ICWSM). After that, he and his advisor, Henry Lieberman, were invited to a White House conference on cyber-bullying on March 18, 2011. "What I learned was that people are so caught up in all the positive benefits that come out of social media: new companies, revenues, how do you monetize this and that, how it has enabled the Arab revolutions," Dinakar says. "But there is definitely a dark side that people don't want to talk about." In particular, there is not a lot of scientific data on cyber-bullying.

MTV, the sponsor of A Thin Line, had representatives at the meeting, and the White House technology officer, Aneesh Chopra, put Dinakar in contact with them. MTV agreed to provide access to a database of 5500 anonymous stories. The stories provide a frank, unvarnished and occasionally startling window into the modern adolescent world:

Story #5069: "*A group of girls are talking about how Im such a 'worthless person' and a bunch of other inappropriate comments, they also are saying how they need to 'take care of it.' I have never said anything about them, but I am being continiously harrased.*"

Story #3770: "*Recently, I have been involved with a boy from a couple towns over. He always asks me to get naked on video chat, so the other night I just took off my top. I didnt know at the time, but he took a picture on his computer and I'm now scared.*"

Using LDA, Dinakar identified the main topics in the corpus (see Figure 7, next page). Sexting, or sending naked pictures over the Internet or cell phone, led the list, appearing in 7.6 percent of the stories. Sometimes the computer did better at identifying topics than Dinakar himself could. "One of the stories said that 'she is forcing me to give up the goods.' I don't know some American slang, so I didn't even know what it meant until my advisor explained that this was code for having sex.

> # In particular, there is not a lot of scientific data on cyber-bullying.

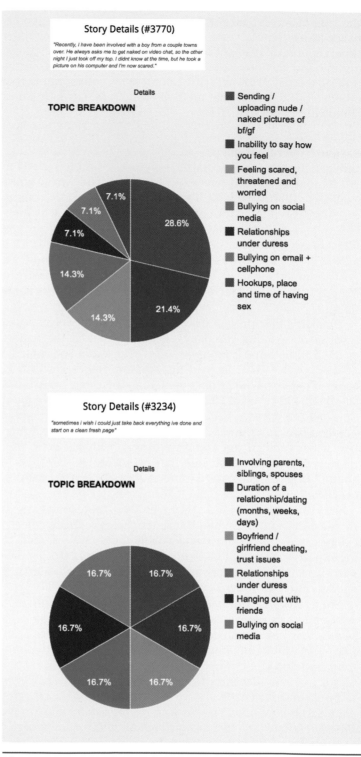

Figure 7. *Topics observed in posts to A Thin Line website, as determined by latent Dirichlet allocation. In posts like #3770, LDA may identify topics better than a keyword search would. On the other hand, post #3234 contains too few clues to figure out what it is about. (Figure courtesy of Karthik Dinakar.)*

The machine was able to find that association on its own." Dinakar also cites this example to explain why topic modeling is better than mere keyword matching. It enables the computer to discover associations, such as the association between "giving up the goods" and sex, that a keyword search would miss.

For a more objective test of the topic assignments, he asked volunteers (either teenagers, professionals who work with children, or machine learning specialists) to compose plausible stories using language from the topic lists. He then had the computer identify thematically similar stories in the corpus, and he asked the volunteers two questions: Did they consider the story a good match, and could they imagine a teenager feeling less alone after reading the related story? More than two-thirds of the stories found by LDA were identified as good matches, and 58 percent were seen as potentially helpful. (By comparison, matches identified by an alternative machine-learning technique were seen as helpful only 8 percent of the time.) "Of course we are hoping to do this with real teenagers who are genuinely depressed, rather than just asking people to imagine," says Dinakar. "That is one of the things we want from MTV."

Whether latent Dirichlet allocation will help to fight cyber-bullying remains to be seen. However, there is no question of the method's ability to find the hidden structure behind texts written by humans. "It's this incredibly simple algorithm, this simple statistical model, that nevertheless seems to get what we mean when we write," says Mimno. "I would put it this way: The algorithm is powerful enough to recognize the human intelligence that put the words in that particular arrangement."

"It's this incredibly simple algorithm, this simple statistical model, that nevertheless seems to get what we mean when we write.....The algorithm is powerful enough to recognize the human intelligence that put the words in that particular arrangement."

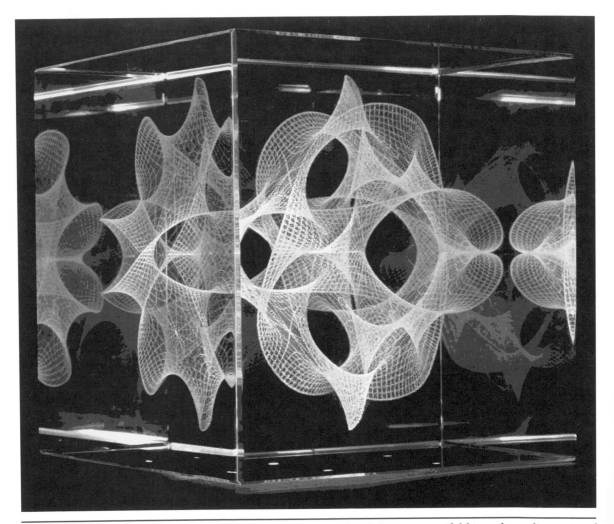

"Calabi-Yau manifold". *A projection of a six-dimensional Calabi-Yau manifold into three-dimensional space, laser-etched in crystal by sculptor Bathsheba Grossman. Calabi-Yau manifolds are fundamental in string theory as a model of what the "extra dimensions" of spacetime might look like. But they are extremely intricate shapes. Tropical geometry may make it possible for mathematicians to study these manifolds using simpler piecewise-linear models. (Figure courtesy of Bathsheba Grossman.)*

Thinking Tropically

"**W**HEN YOU COME TO A FORK IN THE ROAD... Take it." Supposedly this sentence was uttered by the famous baseball player and master of malapropisms, Yogi Berra. If so, it could just be a sign that Yogi was ahead of his time.

According to a new kind of geometry, which was named "tropical geometry" by mathematicians Bernd Sturmfels and Grigory Mikhalkin in 2002, lines are Y-shaped, so it really is possible to "take a fork" in the road. And that's not the only strange thing about tropical mathematics. In tropical algebra the following equation is true:

$$(a \oplus b)^2 = a^2 \oplus b^2.$$

Sturmfels calls this formula "the Freshman Dream," because it is quite possibly the most frequently made mistake by beginning mathematics students. But in tropical algebra, it's not a mistake.

In spite of its apparent eccentricity, writes Erwan Brugallé of the University of Paris at Jussieu, "tropical geometry is not a sterile game for bored mathematicians looking for something to do." In fact, it has turned out to be an ideal venue in which to answer some of the classical questions of algebraic geometry. It is a limiting state in which smooth curves crystallize into polygonal complexes, and difficult problems in analysis become much simpler problems in counting. Though tropical geometry as an independent subject dates back only 10 years, its precursors, such as "patchworking" of real algebraic curves, go back at least to the 1970s.

Perhaps the most tantalizing application of tropical geometry lies in string theory. Physicists hypothesize that what appears to be a point particle (say, an electron) is actually an extremely tiny string that moves about in a 10-dimensional universe. Four of the dimensions are the familiar spacetime we see, while six of the dimensions are tightly coiled into a shape called a Calabi-Yau manifold. As a string moves through these extra six dimensions, it sweeps out a two-dimensional surface inside the Calabi-Yau manifold, called a Riemann surface.[1] An example would be the surface swept out in spacetime by a Higgs particle that decays into two photons. A string theorist would represent this history by a tube that bifurcates into two tubes—a Riemann surface that looks like, and is called, a "pair of pants." At present, tropical geometry seems to be the most promising, or at least the simplest, way to enumerate these surfaces.

Bernd Sturmfels. *(Photo courtesy of Bernd Sturmfels.)*

---

[1]These surfaces are two-dimensional when the coordinates are considered real numbers but only one-dimensional when parameterized by complex numbers. So depending on your point of view, they are sometimes referred to as surfaces and sometimes as curves.

Grigory Mikhalkin. *(Photo courtesy of Grigory Mikhalkin.)*

However, it would be a mistake to view tropical geometry merely as a bag of tricks designed to corroborate the calculations of string theory. Tropical geometry has been a breath of fresh air for the whole field of algebraic geometry, providing new approaches to old problems and raising challenging new ones. It has applications to number theory, statistics, and even the study of "family trees" of organisms, which can be reconstructed through the analysis of their genomes. As is often the case, a truly new mathematical idea has ramifications in many different directions.

What's In a Name?

Perhaps the simplest route to tropical *geometry* begins with tropical *algebra*.

Tropical algebra uses the same real numbers that everyone is familiar with, but it posits two different operations on them. The tropical *sum* of two numbers, $a \oplus b$, is just the maximum of the two. (Thus, for instance, $1 \oplus 1 = 1$ and $2 \oplus 5 = 5$.) The tropical *product*, $a \otimes b$, is the ordinary sum. (So $2 \otimes 5 = 7$.) These two operations enjoy almost all of the normal properties of arithmetic, including the distributive law. However, the "multiplicative" identity is 0 and there is no additive identity (although it is sometimes convenient to introduce $-\infty$ for this purpose). Also, there is no subtraction.

Prior to the introduction of tropical geometry, tropical algebra (or "max-plus algebra") had been used sporadically in a variety of applications. "It was invented and re-invented many times, but typically quite far from the core of pure math," says Sturmfels.

Consider, for instance, a train schedule in which the sequence of train departures and arrivals is exactly the same every hour. Let $x(k)$ denote the scheduled time of the k-th event that is supposed to occur each hour. Very often, a certain amount of time, a_{ij}, has to elapse between event i and event j; for example, train 19 might take at least four minutes to get from Bridge B to Station A, or train 3 may not be allowed to proceed over Bridge B until two minutes after train 19 has vacated it. The result of all these constraints is that the scheduled time of event k, $x(k)$, must be greater than or equal to the maximum of all the times $x(i) + a_{ik}$. In terms of max-plus algebra, $x(k)$ is greater than or equal to $a_{1k} \otimes x(1) \oplus a_{2k} \otimes x(2) \oplus ... \oplus a_{nk} \otimes x(n)$. This looks exactly like a matrix product from linear algebra, with tropical addition and multiplication replacing the normal operations.

In fact, as engineer Rob Goverde of the University of Delft has shown, the matrix A has a (unique) eigenvalue λ that represents the minimum amount of time needed to complete all of the actions $x(k)$. If λ is greater than 60 minutes, the timetable is unfeasible and delays will occur. Even if λ is less than 60 minutes, unexpected events could lead to delays. The tropical algebra can be used to identify how resilient the timetable is, which events can be recovered from and which events will propagate throughout the railroad network.

Though tropical algebra was known before 2002, no one had formalized the concept of tropical *geometry*. Geometry deals, of course, with lines and curves, and it is natural to ask what kind of lines and curves would correspond to the operations of tropical algebra. Since an equation of the form $ax + by + c = 0$

determines a line in ordinary planar geometry, might a similar equation, $a \otimes x \oplus b \otimes y \oplus c = 0$, define a line in tropical geometry?

The answer is yes and no. Remember that the real number 0 does not have the same meaning in tropical algebra as it does in ordinary algebra. It is not the additive identity, and the convenient property $0 \otimes x = 0$ does not hold either. The situation is one that arises constantly in tropical geometry, where you cannot slavishly repeat the constructions that work in conventional geometry or algebra. Instead you have to think what you really want to accomplish. *Why* do we want to compute zero sets of polynomials?

For polynomials of one variable, one reason is that we would like to be able to factor them. For example, in max-plus algebra,

$$x^2 \oplus 3 \otimes x \oplus 4 = (x \oplus 1) \otimes (x \oplus 3).$$

[*Note:* Here and later, exponents are used for repeated tropical multiplication, so $x \otimes x$ is written as x^2.] This somewhat surprising result can be understood by translating it into classical algebra. The function on the left is a piecewise linear function, which is equal to 4 when $x \leq 1$, equal to $x + 3$ when $1 \leq x \leq 3$, and equal to $2x$ when $x \geq 3$. Note that the "roots" of the polynomial, 1 and 3, show up as the *corners* in the graph, or the places where *two* of the monomials x^2, $3 \otimes x$, and 4 tie for first place in the competition to be largest. (See Figure 1, next page.)

A similar idea holds for polynomials in two variables. A tropical polynomial $p(x, y)$ is, from the classical point of view, a piecewise linear function. The locus of points where the pieces come together—the edges and corners in the classical graph of $p(x, y)$—are the "roots" of the polynomial $p(x, y)$. As in the one-variable case, these are the points where two or more of its constituent monomials tie for the largest value.

Figure 2, page 117, shows some examples defined by linear, quadratic, and cubic polynomials. A tropical line always consists of three rays pointing south, west, and northeast. This is the prototypical Y shape mentioned earlier (although rotated by 135 degrees from a conventional "Y" on a keyboard). A curve defined by a quadratic polynomial will have two rays pointing northeast, west, and south, joined together by finite line segments. Finally, cubics contain three rays pointing northeast, south, and west. A pattern has started to emerge: the number of infinite rays in each direction matches the degree of the curve.

There are other routes to tropical geometry that lead to the same kind of figures. In one of them, we start with a curve defined by a classical equation, such as $2x + 3y + 1 = 0$, and for every point (x, y) on the curve we plot $(-log_t|x|, -log_t|y|)$, for some small parameter t, including solutions where x and y are complex numbers. The image of the complex curve under this logarithmic transformation forms a region in the plane called an "amoeba." Unlike "tropical geometry," where the word "tropical" is meaningless—it started as a joke by some French mathematicians—in the case of amoebas the name is quite descriptive. The amoeba has a fat part in the center and three legs that get skinnier and skinnier as they stretch out to infinity. As the parameter t approaches zero, the fat nucleus shrinks and the legs become more spindly,

> The situation is one that arises constantly in tropical geometry, where you cannot slavishly repeat the constructions that work in conventional geometry or algebra. Instead you have to think what you really want to accomplish. *Why* do we want to compute zero sets of polynomials?

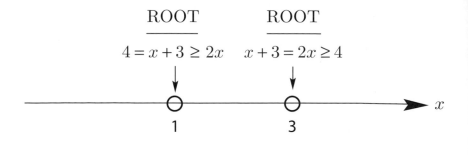

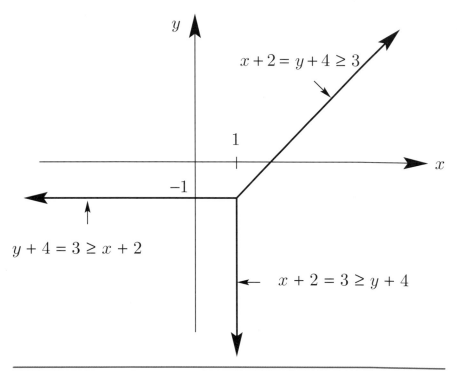

Figure 1. *In tropical geometry, the roots of a polynomial are defined as the points where at least two of its monomials are equal and have values greater than the remaining monomials. (Top) Roots of $p(x) = x^2 \oplus 3 \otimes x \oplus 4 = max\{2x, x + 3, 4\}$. (Bottom) Roots of $p(x, y) = 2 \otimes x \oplus 4 \otimes y \oplus 3 = max\{x + 2, y + 4, 3\}$.*

until in the limit the nucleus becomes a point, the three legs become rays, and the whole figure becomes a tropical line. The small parameter t behaves like Planck's constant in quantum mechanics or the temperature in thermodynamics. One might succinctly say: freeze an amoeba and you get a tropical curve.

The fact that several approaches yield the same tropical curves suggests that the concept is a natural one, even if it appears strange at first. It also suggests that tropical geometry will have more than one application.

New Insights into Old Problems

Classical algebraic geometry deals with curves and surfaces that are defined by polynomial or rational equations (quotients of polynomials). The problems studied include finding their intersections, their mappings, and their parameterizations. ("Parameterizing" a curve or a surface means writing formulas for the coordinates. For example, the circle $x^2 + y^2 = 4$ is parameterized over the complex numbers by $x = t + 1/t$ and $y = i(t - 1/t)$. Note that the more familiar parameterization $x = \cos t$ and $y = \sin t$ is not allowed in algebraic geometry because cosine and sine are not polynomial functions.)

When the variables and coefficients are viewed as complex numbers, algebraic curves behave extraordinarily well. For example, two lines will always intersect in a single point, and two cubics will always intersect in nine points. (There is some fine print concerning intersection points "at infinity" and certain intersections, such as tangencies, that need to be counted more than once.) In general, a plane curve defined by a polynomial of degree p and a curve defined by a polynomial of degree q will always intersect in pq points.

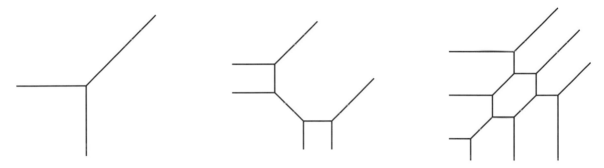

Figure 2. *Tropical lines, conics, and cubics. These are defined as the set of roots of two-variable tropical polynomials of degree 1, 2, and 3 respectively. Though these tropical "curves" are made of straight line segments and rays, they nevertheless share many of the properties of classical curves defined by polynomial equations. (Figures © Erwan Brugallé, Un peu de géométrie tropicale. Quadrature (74), 10–22, 2009. English translation available at http://www.math.jussieu.fr/ ~ brugalle/articles/Quadrature/QuadratureEng.pdf.)*

This fact, called Bezout's theorem, can be proved by defining a single-variable polynomial of degree pq, called the resultant, whose roots correspond to intersection points of the two original curves. By the Fundamental Theorem of Algebra, the resultant polynomial has pq roots (possibly counting some more than once). Thus the curves intersect in pq points (again, possibly counting some with multiplicity). Although Bezout's theorem looks like a theorem in geometry, in fact the whole proof is algebraic.

It may seem unlikely that tropical curves behave so well, but in fact they do. Bezout's theorem has a counterpart in tropical geometry. A pair of lines will still intersect in one point, and a pair of tropical cubics will still intersect in nine points. The proof is quite a bit more elementary, and much more geometric than the classical proof.

The key idea is to construct what is called the dual subdivision to the tropical curve. The monomials in a tropical polynomial $p(x, y)$ have the form $a_{ij} \otimes x^i \otimes y^j$, and each monomial corresponds to a point (i, j) in the plane. These points have integer coordinates, and they all lie in a triangle with vertices at $(0,0)$, $(d, 0)$, and $(0, d)$, where d is the degree of the polynomial. A tropical polynomial $p(x, y)$ defines a subdivision Δ_p of this triangle into smaller pieces, in such a way that each vertex of the tropical "curve" corresponds to a unique cell (called its dual cell) in the subdivision (see Figure 3). Likewise, each line segment or ray leading out from a vertex is perpendicular to one side of its dual cell. In this way, different subdivisions of the reference triangle correspond to different possible shapes for a tropical curve (see Figure 4).

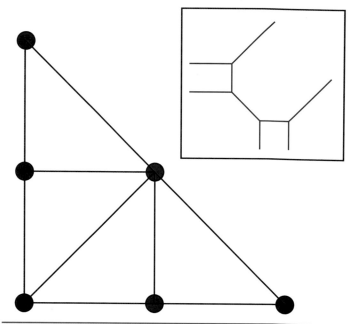

Figure 3. *A tropical conic (red, inset) and its dual subdivision (black). The red curve can be superimposed over its dual subdivision in such a way that each line segment or ray in the curve is perpendicular to a unique line segment in the dual subdivision, and each of the four vertices in the curve lies in the interior of one of the cells in the dual subdivision. (Figures © Erwan Brugallé, Un peu de géométrie tropicale. Quadrature (74), 10–22, 2009. English translation available at http://www.math.jussieu.fr/ ~ brugalle/articles/Quadrature/QuadratureEng.pdf.)*

The product of two tropical polynomials, $p_1(x, y) \otimes p_2(x, y)$, corresponds to the union of two tropical curves. This union has two different kinds of vertices: the ones that were originally vertices of p_1 or p_2 (which are typically Y-shaped) and the points where p_1 and p_2 cross (which are X-shaped). Corresponding to these vertices, the dual subdivision $\Delta_{p_1 p_2}$ has two different kinds of cells. The cells that correspond to vertices of p_1 or p_2 will match a corresponding cell in Δ_{p_1} or Δ_{p_2}. The other kind of cell corresponds to a crossing point, and this type is always a parallelogram of area 1. By adding the areas of all the cells, you can show that the total area of the parallelograms (and therefore the number of intersection points) equals $d_1 d_2$.

In 2002, Mikhalkin proved tropical analogues for several other classic counting theorems in algebraic geometry. The prototypical non-tropical problem specifies a set of points, a degree d, and a topological type (given by the genus g) and asks: how many curves of degree d and genus g pass through the given set of points? For example, two points determine a unique line, and five points determine a unique conic.

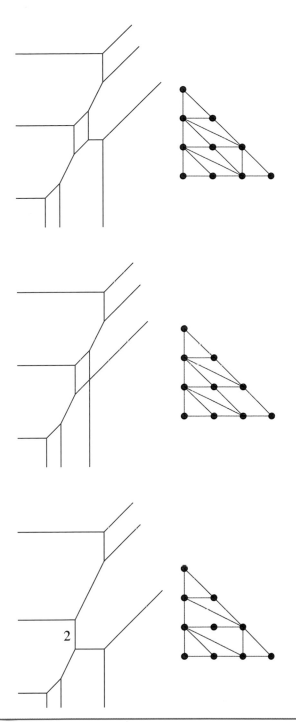

Figure 4. *The possible shapes of a tropical cubic can be classified by the dual subdivisions. In the middle figure, notice that the "X" shaped intersection corresponds to a parallelogram in the dual subdivision. In the bottom figure, notice that one line segment of the cubic is counted with a double multiplicity. This corresponds to a line segment in the dual subdivision that passes through a lattice point. (Figures © Erwan Brugallé, Un peu de géométrie tropicale. Quadrature (74), 10-22, 2009. English translation available at http://www.math.jussieu.fr/ ~ brugalle/articles/Quadrature/QuadratureEng.pdf.)*

With cubics, both classical and tropical, the answer becomes less obvious, in part because the genus can be either zero or one.[2] In classical algebraic geometry, there is a unique genus-1 cubic passing through nine points, but there are 12 genus-0 cubics passing through a generic set of eight points. Mikhalkin showed that *the same theorem is true for tropical cubics*, provided that some of the curves are counted more than once in a prescribed way (see Figure 5).

(a)

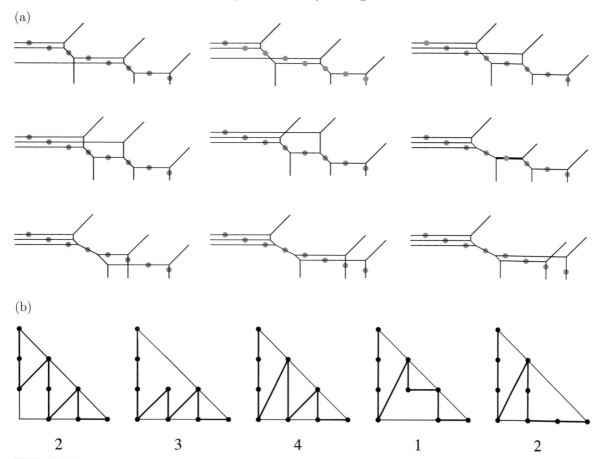

(b)

| 2 | 3 | 4 | 1 | 2 |

Figure 5. *(a) Given eight points in the plane (blue dots) it is possible to find twelve tropical cubics of genus 0 passing through them. The sixth curve, which has a double side, has to be counted four times. (b) Mikhalkin's proof begins by constructing all the 8-step paths from the upper left corner to the lower right corner in the dual subdivision. Numbers below the paths indicate how many of the curves in part (a) correspond to the indicated path. (Figure courtesy of the European Mathematical Society.)*

Mikhalkin's method begins by enumerating the possible 8-step paths that lead from the upper left corner of the reference triangle to the lower right corner. As shown in Figure 5(b), there are five such paths. Each step in the paths corresponds to one of the colored points in Figure 5(a). For example, in the first of these paths (labeled "2"), the first step in the path corresponds to the left-most point in Figure 5(a) Notice that the ray passing through this point is horizontal, and the first step in the 8-step

---

[2]A tropical cubic will have genus 1 if its curve contains a loop, or equivalently if all of its vertices are Y-shaped. If it has one X-shaped intersection point (called a node) then its genus is 0.

path in Figure 5(b) is vertical. Similarly, for each of the other colored points, the line segment or ray passing through that point in Figure 5(a) is perpendicular to the corresponding segment in Figure 5(b).

Once the eight colored points have segments or rays drawn through them in the appropriate directions, there are only finitely many ways to join these segments up into a valid tropical cubic. For the first path in Figure 5(b), labeled "2", there are two ways to join the segments together, and they give the first two cubics illustrated in Figure 5(a). For the second path in Figure 5(b), labeled "3", there are three ways to join the segments together, which produce the third through fifth cubics in Figure 5(a). The third path in Figure 5(b) is a special case. It contains a segment of length 2 that passes through a lattice point. This corresponds to the extra-dark segment in the sixth cubic, which is to be counted with multiplicity 2. By Mikhalkin's rules of counting (which are too technical to explain here), this entire cubic must be counted four times. Finally, paths four and five produce the remaining three cubics seen in Figure 5(a). The total number of cubics is 12, taking into account the fact that the sixth cubic was counted four times.

This procedure, including the technical details for counting curves multiple times, can be generalized to curves of any degree and genus. For example, Figure 6 shows the first step for enumerating the 225 quartics (degree-four curves) of genus 1 passing through 12 given points.

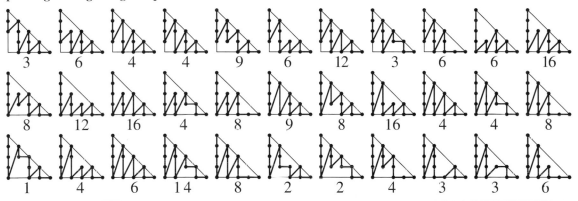

Figure 6. *Mikhalkin's procedure can be used to solve other curve-counting problems in tropical geometry. For example, there are 225 genus-1 quartics passing through 12 given points. Their construction begins by listing all the 12-step paths leading from the upper left corner to the lower right corner of the dual subdivision. (Figure courtesy of Grigory Mikhalkin. From G. Mikhalkin, "Enumerative tropical geometry in R^2," Journal of the American Mathematical Society, 2005.)*

These calculations play an important role in string theory. The number of genus-zero curves through a finite set of points (12 cubics through eight points, 620 quartics through eleven points, etc.) is called a Gromov-Witten invariant, after geometer Mikhael Gromov and string theorist Ed Witten. Methods for computing Gromov-Witten invariants were known before tropical geometry, but "Mikhalkin's result was a big breakthrough," says Mark Gross, a tropical geometry expert at the University of California at San Diego. "It's a simple procedure, and somewhat miraculous that this completely combinatorial counting procedure works in the plane for every degree and genus."

In 1900, David Hilbert proposed a list of 23 unsolved problems that motivated mathematical research throughout the twentieth century. Number sixteen on the list asked (in part) to classify the shapes of all the curves in the real plane given by polynomials of degree d**. This is actually a very old problem: even Isaac Newton had worked on this problem for the case of cubics.**

Bezout's theorem and the Gromov-Witten invariants are only two of the many exciting applications or analogues between tropical geometry and classical algebraic geometry. Here, in brief, are three more:

1) HILBERT'S SIXTEENTH PROBLEM.

In 1900, David Hilbert proposed a list of 23 unsolved problems that motivated mathematical research throughout the twentieth century. Number sixteen on the list asked (in part) to classify the shapes of all the curves in the real plane given by polynomials of degree d. This is actually a very old problem: even Isaac Newton had worked on this problem for the case of cubics.

When the variables x and y are real numbers, algebraic curves do not behave in as tidy a fashion as they do over the complex numbers. As the degree increases, Hilbert's problem degenerates into a dizzying list of cases, which has confounded even the greatest mathematical minds in history. Newton identified 72 different shapes of cubic curves but missed six. Hilbert himself missed one of the possible shapes for curves defined by degree-six polynomials. A curve of this shape was discovered by Dmitry Gudkov in 1969.

To date, Hilbert's problem has been solved only up to degree 7. One of the key challenges, as Gudkov's example shows, is proving the *existence* of curves of a given combinatorial type. In the 1970s, Oleg Viro invented a technique called "patchworking" that constructs curves from a scaffold made up of straight line segments. These scaffolds are nothing more than curves in tropical geometry (though they were of course not called by that name at the time). His technique anticipated Mikhalkin's correspondence principle, which says that a tropical curve always corresponds to some classical curve of a similar combinatorial type and vice versa. Tropical geometry, together with Mikhalkin's correspondence principle, greatly clarified Viro's patchworking technique and Gudkov's construction (see Figure 7, page 123, and Figure 8, page 124).

2) ELIMINATION OF VARIABLES AND IMPLICITIZATION.

Another classical problem of algebraic geometry is the solution of systems of polynomial equations, and this is in fact what got Sturmfels interested in tropical geometry. The classical proof of Bezout's theorem shows how a system of two polynomials in two variables can be reduced to one polynomial (the resultant) in one variable. This approach is computationally very clumsy, because the resultant polynomial is enormous. By contrast, the geometrical approach, exemplified by the tropical proof of Bezout's theorem, seems much more elementary and suitable for computer calculation.

A recent success of Sturmfels' school has come in a related problem called implicitization: Given a plane curve $(x(t), y(t))$, parameterized by rational functions (quotients of polynomials), can you find an implicit equation $f(x, y) = 0$ for the curve? This problem, and its higher-dimensional versions, can be solved elegantly using tropical geometry. The dual subdivision, which was so useful for Bezout's problem, is now replaced by *Newton's polygon*, which records all of the exponent pairs

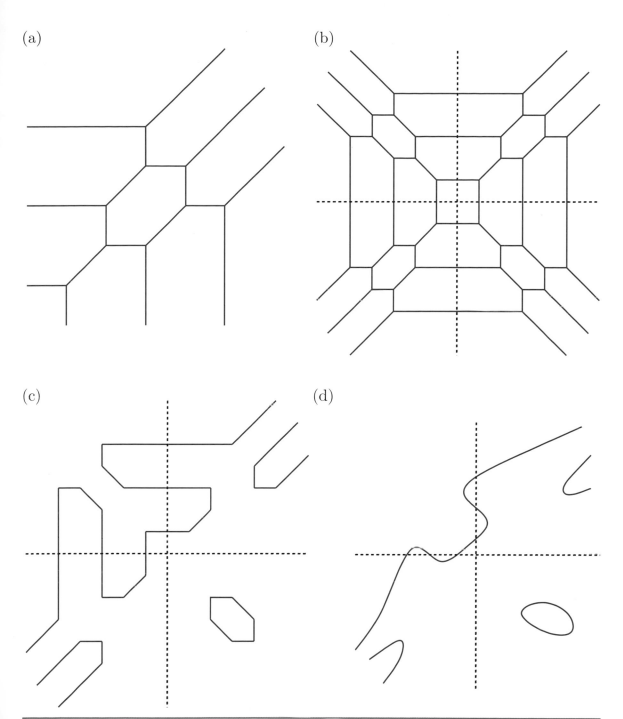

Figure 7. *Oleg Viro's "patchworking" technique for constructing real algebraic curves, interpreted in terms of tropical geometry. (a) A tropical cubic. (b) The cubic is reflected four times. (c) Half of the line segments and rays are erased according to a specific set of rules. (d) Mikhalkin's correspondence principle says that a classical (real) cubic must exist whose combinatorial type is the same as the "patchwork" figure in part (c). (Figures ©Erwan Brugallé, Un peu de géométrie tropicale. Quadrature (74), 10-22, 2009. English translation available at http://www.math.jussieu.fr/~brugalle/articles/Quadrature/QuadratureEng.pdf.)*

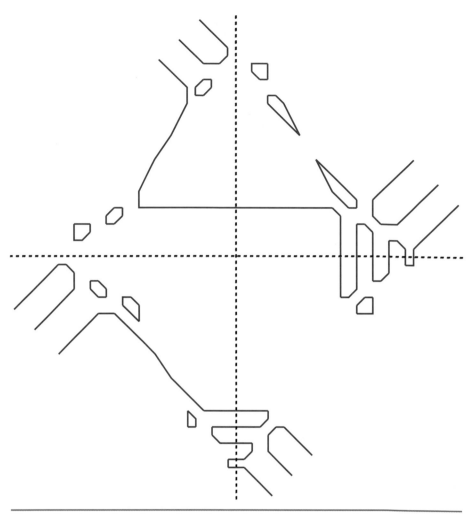

Figure 8. *A patchwork version of a real algebraic curve of degree 6 that was believed by David Hilbert to be impossible. Specifically, it has five small "islands" between the two longest meandering curves and five outside them. Hilbert believed that the islands had to be distributed with nine between and one outside, or vice versa. (Figures © Erwan Brugallé, Un peu de géométrie tropicale. Quadrature (74), 10-22, 2009. English translation available at http://www.math.jussieu.fr/ ~ brugalle/articles/Quadrature/QuadratureEng.pdf.)*

(i, j) that occur in nonzero monomials $a_{ij} \otimes x^i \otimes y^j$ of $f(x, y)$. In a sense, tropical geometry allows you to squint your eyes and look at the curve from "infinitely far away," so that the specific coefficients a_{ij} don't matter; all you see are the exponents. Once you have discovered which exponents occur in the implicit function, it is an easy linear algebra problem to find the coefficients. The method was developed by Sturmfels and Jenia Tevelev and implemented in a program called TrIm (Tropical Implicitization) by Sturmfels' former student, Josephine Yu.

3) THE BRILL-NOETHER THEOREM.

Another problem of classical algebraic geometry is the mapping of algebraic curves into higher-dimensional spaces. "The fundamental question is for which triples d, g, r does every algebraic curve of genus g admit a map of degree d to the projective space of dimension r?" says Sam Payne of Yale University.

In 1870, Alexander von Brill and Max Noether correctly stated that such maps existed if and only if $g \geq (r + 1)(g - d + r)$, but according to Payne, "They did not give any proof that would hold up to modern standards, just a back-of-the-envelope calculation." They predicted that the dimension of the space of such maps should be the difference between g and $(r + 1)(g - d + r)$. But what if that dimension is negative? Intuitively, that should mean there are no such maps, because the only set with "negative dimension" is the empty set. However, this hardly qualifies as a proof.

The "nonexistence" part of the Brill-Noether theorem was first put on solid ground by Phillip Griffiths and Joseph Harris in 1980. In 2011, Payne and three collaborators (Filip Cools, Jan Draisma, and Elina Robeva) re-proved it using tropical geometry. "This is actually the fourth fundamentally different proof," Payne says. "Reasonable people could disagree on which one is simplest."

Payne and his colleagues tropicalized a random genus-g curve into a graph of a very special type: a chain of g loops with random edge lengths. If the curve had a map of degree d to r-dimensional space, then the inverse images of hyperplanes (i.e., $(r - 1)$ dimensional planes) would be configurations of d points on the tropical curve. As the hyperplanes move around, so do the d-point configurations, by a specific sequence of moves known as "chip-firing." The combinatorics of chip-firing has been studied in great detail by graph theorists, with no knowledge of its possible application to algebraic geometry.

Ultimately they showed that a chain of loops with random edge lengths does not admit enough chip-firing moves, and therefore the supposed map to r-dimensional space does not exist. A technical statement called "Baker's specialization lemma" (after Matthew Baker of Georgia Institute of Technology) allowed them to transfer their combinatorial nonexistence result about chains of g loops into a nonexistence result about genus-g curves. This kind of bridge-building theorem, similar to Mikhalkin's correspondence theorem, seems to be essential if you want to prove theorems about classical curves and surfaces from simpler tropical constructions.

The Tree of Life, and the Backbone of Physics

In addition to its many applications within pure mathematics, tropical geometry has begun to find some uses in biology and physics.

In the 2000s, the availability of cheap and fast gene sequencing has made it possible for biologists to quantify the evolutionary distance between species. For example, the distance between the mouse and rat genomes might be 0.3 in appropriate units, while the distance from humans to mice is greater, say 1.0 units, and the distance from humans to chickens is even greater than that, say 1.4.

According to the theory of evolution, all of these species are descended from some common ancestor, and so the question arises: how far removed, in genomic terms, is that ancestor, and in what order did the species branch off from one another? Intuitively, we would expect that the chickens split first, then the humans, and last the mice and rats (see Figure 9a, page 127).

The "phylogenetic tree" is literally what mathematicians call a tree: namely, it is a graph with no loops. Each speciation event

> In addition to its many applications within pure mathematics, tropical geometry has begun to find some uses in biology and physics.

**The Four Point
Condition was known
by biologists
previously. But
expressing it in terms of
tropical geometry
opened up several new
possibilities.**

corresponds to a Y-shaped fork in the tree. Each edge of this graph has a certain length assigned to it, and the distance between two species is assumed to be the length of the (unique) path joining them.

The fact that species are vertices on a mathematical tree leads to an interesting constraint on the evolutionary distances between them, called the Four Point Condition. Pick any four points on a tree graph—points 1, 2, 3, and 4—and split them into pairs. Now add the distances between the points in each pair, to get the numbers $d_{12} + d_{34}, d_{13} + d_{24}$, and $d_{14} + d_{23}$. No matter what the distances are, two of these three numbers will turn out to be equal to each other and greater than or equal to the third. (see Figure 9b). In the language of tropical geometry, the maximum of $d_{12} \otimes d_{34}, d_{13} \otimes d_{24}$, and $d_{14} \otimes d_{23}$ is achieved twice, so the distances $(d_{12}, d_{13}, d_{14}, d_{23}, d_{24}, d_{34})$ lie on the tropical hypersurface defined by the polynomial

$$(d_{12} \otimes d_{34}) \oplus (d_{13} \otimes d_{24}) \oplus (d_{14} \otimes d_{23}).$$

The Four Point Condition was known by biologists previously. But expressing it in terms of tropical geometry opened up several new possibilities. First, Sturmfels and David Speyer proved that these conditions are in fact *sufficient* as well as necessary: if the taxonomic distances you have measured satisfy this condition (for any four out of n species), then it is guaranteed that you can find an evolutionary tree for all n species that is consistent with the data. Sturmfels and Lior Pachter proved the stronger result that the evolutionary tree can be reconstructed from dissimilarity measures among larger sets of species, rather than just pairs. Finally, in any case involving real data there will be small chance errors, and so the Four Point Condition will not be precisely satisfied. The biologists had developed a neighbor-joining algorithm to find a tree that is roughly consistent with the data. The algorithm works quite well but until the advent of tropical geometry it had not been entirely clear, from a geometric point of view, how it worked.

Finally, the connections between tropical geometry and physics were mentioned above in the context of the Gromov-Witten invariants. However, they may in fact go quite a bit deeper. One of the most extraordinary early discoveries of string theory was a phenomenon called mirror symmetry, a mysterious correspondence between pairs of Calabi-Yau manifolds that reduces curve-counting on one manifold to an integral on a related manifold called its "mirror dual." A group led by physicist Phillip Candelas in 1991 used this strategy to compute a whole series of invariants, similar to Gromov-Witten invariants, that mathematicians not only could not compute, but could not even prove were finite. In this instance, physicists had left mathematicians in the dust. However, their methods were not (and still are not) considered rigorous, and that meant mathematicians had to cobble up some new geometry to explain what was going on.

"These predictions were proved in 1996 by [Alexander] Givental, but there was a lack of understanding of why they worked," says Gross. At present nobody knows how general the phenomenon of mirror symmetry is, how to find or construct the mirror manifold, and how to justify this kind of reduction.

However, tropical geometry is one of the best candidates for finding an answer. To begin with, tropical geometry is ideal for curve counting, as shown by the Gromov-Witten invariants. Also, one hypothesized explanation of mirror symmetry, called the Strominger-Yau-Zaslow (SYZ) Conjecture, posits that a six-dimensional Calabi-Yau manifold has a three-dimensional backbone, or base manifold, of half the dimension. Attached to this backbone is a family of ribs, which would be three-dimensional tori that may be pinched in various ways. According to the SYZ Conjecture, any Calabi-Yau manifold and its twin actually have the same backbone, but the ribs are attached differently. If so, perhaps tropical geometry could be used as an "X-ray machine" to identify the backbone and ribs. More precisely, Mikhalkin hopes that the backbone would be a tropical manifold, and the "ribs" would be obtained from what mathematicians call its tangent and cotangent spaces.

This conjectural picture of mirror symmetry still has many uncertainties, as does the subject of tropical geometry itself. Even the definition of n-dimensional tropical surfaces in an $(n + k)$-dimensional space, for general n and k, has not been completely agreed upon yet. But this uncertainty suits Mikhalkin just fine. "In my experience, a new area of mathematics is the most fun while it is still not too well-understood," he says. "Once the theory becomes well-developed it is less fun. In tropical geometry we have an open space ahead." Or perhaps a road with plenty of forks?

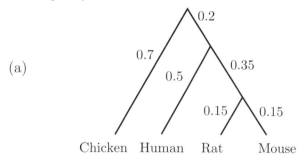

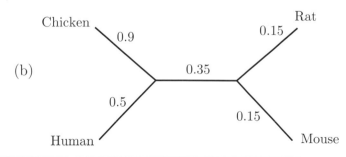

Figure 9. *An application of tropical geometry to phylogenetic trees. (a) Evolutionary distances between species on a conventional "tree of life." (b) The Four Point Condition, a necessary and sufficient condition for consistency of evolutionary distances. Note that d(Chicken, Mouse) + d(Human, Rat) = 2.4 = d(Chicken, Rat) + d(Human, Mouse) but d(Chicken, Human) + d(Mouse, Rat) = 1.7 < 2.4.*

MATHEMATICAL MOMENTS

Being on the Cutting Edge

Cutters of diamonds and other gemstones have a high-pressure job with conflicting demands: Flaws must be removed from rough stones to maximize brilliance but done so in a way that yields the greatest weight possible. Because diamonds are often cut to a standard shape, cutting them is far less complex than cutting other gemstones, such as rubies or sapphires, which can have hundreds of different shapes. By coupling geometry and multivariable calculus with optimization techniques, mathematicians have been able to devise algorithms that automatically generate precise cutting plans that maximize brilliance and yield.

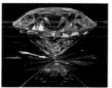

www.ams.org/mathmoments

Getting a Handle on Obesity

Once a problem only in the developed world, obesity is now a worldwide epidemic. The overwhelming cause of the epidemic is a dramatic increase in the food supply and in food consumption—not a surprise. Yet there are still many mysteries about weight change that can't be answered either inside the lab, because of the impracticality of keeping people isolated for long periods of time, or outside, because of the unreliability of dietary diaries. Mathematical models based on differential equations can help overcome this roadblock and allow detailed analysis of the relationship between food intake, metabolism, and weight change. The models' predictions fit existing data and explain such things as why it is so hard to keep weight off and why obese people are more susceptible to further weight gain.

www.ams.org/mathmoments

Putting the Auto in Automobile

It may be hard to accept but it's likely that we'd all be much safer in autonomous vehicles driven by computers, not humans. Annually more than 30,000 Americans die in car crashes, almost all due to human error. Autonomous vehicles will communicate position and speed to each other and avoid potential collisions—without the possibility of dozing off or road rage. There are still many legal (and insurance) issues to resolve, but researchers who are revving up the development of autonomous vehicles are relying on geometry for recognizing and tracking objects, probability to assess risk, and logic to prove that systems will perform as required.

www.ams.org/mathmoments

Forecasting Crime

No one can predict who will commit a crime but in some cities math is helping detect areas where crimes have the greatest chance of occurring. Police then increase patrols in these "hot spots" in order to prevent crime. This innovative practice called predictive policing is based on large amounts of data collected from previous crimes, but it involves more than just maps and push pins. Predictive policing identifies hot spots by using algorithms similar to those used to predict aftershocks after major earthquakes. Just as aftershocks are more likely near a recent earthquake's epicenter, so too are crimes, as criminals do indeed return to, or very close to, the scene of a crime.

www.ams.org/mathmoments

Catching and Releasing

There's more mathematics involved in juggling than just trying to make sure that the number of balls (or chainsaws) that hits the ground stays at zero. Subjects such as combinatorics and abstract algebra help jugglers answer important questions, such as whether a particular juggling pattern can actually be juggled. For example, can balls be juggled so that the time period that each ball stays aloft alternates between five counts and one? The answer is "Yes." Math also tells you that the number of balls needed for such a juggling pattern is the average of the counts, in this case three.

www.ams.org/mathmoments

Finding Friends

Facebook has over 700 million users with almost 70 billion connections. The hard part isn't people making friends; rather it's Facebook's computers storing and accessing relevant data, including information about friends of friends. The latter is important for recommendations to users (People You May Know). Much of this work involves computer science, but mathematics also plays a significant role. Subjects such as linear programming and graph theory help cut in half the time needed to determine a person's friends of friends and reduce network traffic on Facebook's machines by about two-thirds. What's not to like!

www.ams.org/mathmoments

See 100 Mathematical Moments, **hear** people talk about how they use math on the job in the modern world, and **read translations** in 13 languages at

www.ams.org/mathmoments

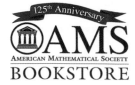